FIESTA LETTERS

Jim and I have been married for three and a half years. We are both 28 years old and have no children. What I want to tell you about happened when we were on holiday in Brighton. One night I was looking through the evening paper for something to do and I noticed an advertisement for a new sauna proclaiming that that night would be a mixed session.

I had better explain at this point that Jim has always liked me to flaunt myself — wearing sexy clothes when we go out to clubs, showing plenty of leg and cleavage. He once admitted to me that the letters he liked most in Fiesta *were those where wives flirted with other men in front of their husbands, and I have done this once or twice myself.*

We arrived at the sauna at about eight o'clock and found the place almost empty. Jim and I both got stripped off in the communal changing rooms and made our way to the sauna. There were two men already in there and their eyes nearly popped out of their heads when I took my towel off. Though I say so myself, I do have a good figure . . .

Joan, Glasgow

Also available in Star

THE FIESTA BOOK OF SAUCY CROSSWORDS

THE
FIESTA LETTERS

Edited by Chris Lloyd

A STAR BOOK
Published by
the Paperback Division of
W.H. ALLEN & Co. PLC.

A Star Book
Published in 1986
by the Paperback Division of
W.H. Allen & Co. PLC
44 Hill Street, London W1X 8LB
Reprinted 1986 (twice)

Copyright © Fiesta 1986

Printed and bound in Great Britain by
Anchor Brendon Ltd, Tiptree, Essex

ISBN 0 352 31729 9

Dedicated to Tom, Dick, Harry. . .
and Dirty Delia of Staffs

Introduction

Once upon a time (approximately three years ago), I had a conversation with a taxi driver. He was taking me to Marble Arch. I had an appointment, and was in a hurry. Apparently he wasn't, and thus we went there via the scenic route. The conversation went like this:

'So you're the editor of that *Fiesta*, are you?'

There was only one way to answer that, so I said I was.

'OK, chief,' he went on, 'there's one question I've been meaning to ask you guys. Those letters you print, you know all the sex stuff and what they all get up to. Are they, like, genuine?'

'You think I write them all myself?' I asked him.

'Well, I. . .' he gave an embarrassed snort. He obviously thought so.

'I don't have the stamina. Or the imagination.'

'OK, who does then?'

'They do.'

'Who?'

'The readers.'

'You mean. . .?'

'Yes. They sit down with a pen at home, and sometimes their wife is leaning over their shoulder with encouragement, or at the office during a lunch break, or when they're killing time at a hotel between engagements, or during an evening when there's nothing on the TV. And they write down what happened to them on the way to the launderette or when they came home early to find the odd-job man upstairs in mid-copulatory stride with a woman they believed was frigid. Sometimes they'll put down what ought to have happened if they'd had long enough to think about it. Sometimes they'll pretend it did

6

happen. Sometimes it's a recurring dream. Anything. The main thing is, they put it in an envelope, attach a stamp and send it to my office.'

'So you don't make them up?'

'That's right. I don't make them up.'

'I see.'

But he didn't. It's hard to believe, I suppose. But confession, they tell me, is good for the soul. And thus the pages of *Fiesta* are filled with the thoughts, desires, fetishes, hopes and wildest fantasies of a general public well-aware that others are doing it, so why shouldn't they? Maybe they write it down because they can't believe it actually happened. Maybe they do it because they want other people to know what they did. Maybe they want it in print because no one else in their lives is listening to them, or wishes to listen. Who knows?

That's all fine with me. I just have one complaint. If it isn't possible for all these letter writers to get hold of a typewriter, would it be too much to ask that I could read them without an awful, sinking suspicion that I am going blind?

Chris Lloyd,
Editor/*Fiesta*

1. THREE'S COMPANY

Call Of The Wild
Keeping It Up
Do It In The Rhodes
Smut & Geoff
Pedallo Power
Four Friends
Lone Ranger
The Thirty-eight Steps
Upstairs Downstairs
Spreading The Marj
Cum On Eileen
All Steamed Up

The Postman Always Comes
  Twice
Men At Work
Flash In The Van
Office Rocker
Spur Of The Moment
French Leave
Finding Out
Birthday Treat
Secret Life
Slide Show

Call Of The Wild

Gerald of Derbyshire's letter in Vol. 18 No. 5 reminds me of a similar experience I had last summer. My young wife Marilyn and I were taking a walk in the early evening just as it was getting dark. We'd had a couple of lagers each, and no wonder we both felt like peeing.

Fortunately (and unfortunately) we found a toilet, but there was only a Gents. I went in while my poor wife had to wait outside. When I emerged, I suggested she go into a cubicle as there was no one there, and it didn't look as if any others would visit. Reluctantly she agreed — the call of nature was such. I stood outside the cubicle, ready for another pee.

After about a minute or so, Marilyn said she was amazed at the filth written on the walls. She began reading a few out loud, and I got a hard-on while she read 'I love watching my wife being fucked by teenage boys.' Of course, some were gay messages, and these she ignored. But there were drawings of large cocks which amused her and, I suspect, turned her on.

Just then a youngish lad walked in — must have been about 19 or so — tall and blond haired. Wasn't he surprised to see me sporting a hard-on! But when he heard my wife say 'Listen to this one: "My wife sucks off my best mate — his is ten inches long",' he was gasping. I merely smiled. And then my wife, quite unaware of this visitor, remarked 'It seems most guys get turned on giving their wives to other blokes. What about you?' By this time the young 'intruder' was finding it difficult concealing *his* hard-on.

By looking at it (it was unavoidable) I realised it was

quite massive — much larger than my own six inches. About half as big again, I'd say. In answer to my wife, I beckoned to the lad to move nearer the cubicle. I knocked on the door and asked her to open it, saying I wanted to read some myself. Can you imagine her surprise when she saw this young blond guy stood there, with this huge erection pointing at her? She gasped.

I said to her I just might be one of those liberated type husbands. I guided the lad in and he didn't resist. Although Marilyn is nearly 34, she is in superb condition, with a pair of lovely boobs and a generally very acceptable pair of legs. I entered myself, and because of the lack of space this lad and my wife just pressed against each other. Soon they French kissed, and my randy wife cupped his dick. I watched and began wanking furiously.

Having tasted his young mouth, my loving wife knelt before him and began tasting his tool. She licked at its huge shiny knob and then gingerly fitted it into her mouth. She knew what I was doing. Then she asked the lad to come in her mouth. 'Go on, I want you to spunk in my mouth, like the mate of the author on the wall does to his wife.' This graffiti was having a remarkable effect on her.

But the guy, who hardly spoke, had other ideas! He raised her up and pushed her against the wall. Her knickers were already off (remember? She'd gone for a pee) and she rested one leg on the loo, so that her delightful pussy was open for a fuck. The lad stepped forward and guided his dong in. It took a little bit of effort, but I had the shameless thrill of watching a 19-year-old's big cock enter my wife's cunt in a public lavatory. I was going berserk!

The lad moved nicely — looked as if he probably played a few sports. My wife wrapped her arm around his neck and clung to him as she swore her first orgasm at him. She came like a volcano, and then came off again. Then she dropped to her knees and began to wank the lad off, pointing the knob at her face. She slipped her mouth over the swollen, shiny knob and pumped her attractive dark head, nice and hard.

He gasped and came off — a few evil spurts in her mouth, and then drenched her lovely features with a torrent. She sucked his cock till not a drop was spared. By this time I was in a rage. I shot my load all over the graffiti-ridden wall, watched by the two performers.

My wife, courteous and polite, thanked the lad for a nice time. He was a bit embarrassed, but thanked us both. I asked him for his name and phone number — just in case, as I put it 'My wife fancies a bit on the side again.' We have since called the lad over three or four times, meeting up in a nearby park for a good gobble. I watch and keep my eyes open for intruders — though that seems a bit pointless, as Greg himself was an intruder.

On one occasion they had it off in the grass, both fully clothed, in the old-fashioned missionary style. Surely the 'call of nature' has to be answered!

Edward, Kent

Keeping Up

Until recently my husband Neil has always made me shave my pussy, but something happened a few months ago to change that. I am rather small, only five feet in my stockinged feet, dark haired, and quite hairy I suppose.

As I said, my husband always insisted on shaving me every three weeks or so. But this changed when I went to stay with my sister, who was unwell, and it meant me staying away from home for two nights. The day I returned home, I crept into the house quite early in the morning. I was going to surprise my husband — but I was the one who got the surprise when I peeped around the bedroom door to find Neil making love to Ros, our next door neighbour.

I was absolutely dumbstruck. I just watched for a while as they grunted away, oblivious of me, then I crept away. I went round to a nearby telephone box then and phoned

Neil to say I was on my way home from my sister's.

Neil didn't say anything when I got back and there was no sign of Ros. I decided to set a trap, and I made a big point of saying I was going out the next day and would not be back until late.

As soon as Neil left for work the following day, I set about making the airing cupboard into a suitable hiding place. I kept watching out of the window all day long, and when Neil finally appeared about 2 o'clock I rushed upstairs and climbed into my hiding place.

When Neil came into the house he shouted my name a few times. A short while later I heard him coming up the stairs talking to someone — and I knew who! The airing cupboard has slats in the door and I could see quite clearly into our bedroom.

Neil immediately proceeded to strip Ros off and eagerly began sucking and licking at her cunt, saying how lovely and hairy she was and how I wouldn't grow my hairs. Then he stripped off himself and Ros took her turn in sucking his prick.

As I watched I started to finger myself. I didn't intend to, I just felt the urge. They then started fucking for ten minutes, and when they had finished they got dressed and went downstairs. I heard the front door slam behind them, so I climbed out of my cubby hole and went downstairs. Then I wanked myself to orgasm, thinking all the time of what I had just witnessed.

Later that night, when Neil was making love to me, I started to talk about my own pubic hair and suggested that I might start growing it again. Neil said that when we first got married it had put him off sucking me, but now he admitted he would quite enjoy it.

As the weeks passed I asked him more and more about what he would like me to do, and, as you can imagine, it was quite a list! We've now swapped partners with our friends, Jim and his wife, and Neil has even brought a colleague home from work and he fucked me while Neil watched.

So the advice I give to all women is, find out what your man likes — or you'll lose him.

Lynda, Nottingham

Do It In The Rhodes

My wife Sheila and myself were nearing the end of a splendid holiday in Rhodes. I am thirty-five years old and Sheila is thirty. Quite early on the holiday we had befriended a good looking young man called Noel, who throughout the holiday had little luck with the girls, and complained to us that he had no technique. He also mentioned that he suffered from premature ejaculation.

Two days before we were due to leave for home, it was his birthday and we invited him to our room for a celebration drink. Sheila was wearing a white mini-dress which looked super against her bronzed legs, and a pair of white transparent panties. We had decided the previous evening to help Noel with his problem, so I made an excuse shortly after he arrived and I left, saying I had to go and hire a car. Instead, however, I hid myself in the bathroom and waited to see what happened, watching what went on in the bedroom with the aid of a large, well positioned mirror.

First of all, Sheila left Noel sitting on the bed as she bent down to the bottom drawer, as if reaching to get something from it. Of course her skirt rode up high and her bottom, encased in the skimpy panties, was revealed to Noel's interested gaze. Returning to him, she pretended to lose her balance and fell across him on the bed with her legs apart revealing her moist cunt to his gaze.

Before he said anything she took his hand and moved it onto her breast, and after being initially startled Noel joined in and was soon sliding his other hand up her naked thighs and nibbling her ear. He began to stroke my wife's moist cunt through the flimsy material of her panties, and then pulled the gusset to one side and slid his fingers into her moist hole.

Sheila moved away and pulled Noel to his feet, revealing a great erection bulging in the front of his trousers. Kneeling in front of him, she unzipped his trousers, eased them down his legs and then slowly removed them together with his pants. His prick was very hard, slim and about six inches long. I noticed that he was already breathing very hard when Sheila took his knob into her mouth, sucking and playing with it as she ran her nails up and down his shaft and gently kneaded his balls. Suddenly, he cried out and shot his come into her mouth.

She moved him over to the bed, pushed him onto it and then proceeded to slowly strip in front of him. First she unzipped her dress teasingly, lifting it off above her head and letting it drop to the floor. Naturally she wasn't wearing a bra and her breasts looked superb with their nipples hard and erect. Sheila sat on a chair in front of Noel, opened her legs wide and began to stroke her cunt through her panties. She slipped her fingers inside her moist slit and began to rub herself off in front of Noel, who looked on in amazement.

With this show, his prick was very soon erect once more. Sheila noticed it standing firm and crossed over to the bed, lying on it beside Noel. Without prompting, he took her in his arms and kissed her hard, letting his hand fall between her legs. Soon his fingers were busily working in and out and, moving to a kneeling position beside my wife, he slipped off her panties as she raised her bottom to assist, then he began lapping at her cunt. Before long Sheila was moaning gently with pleasure, and Noel moved up her body and slid his firm prick deep into her longing cunt.

No premature ejaculation this time. He rode and fucked her for well over five minutes and Sheila was almost shrieking as she peaked with pleasure before he shot his spunk deep into her moist eager cunt. He lay in her arms, and his cream slowly dribbled out of her hole, Sheila rubbed it into her thighs.

15

I appeared soon afterwards, having tossed myself off in the bathroom whilst watching. Before Noel could get embarrassed we explained to him that he had just had his birthday treat, and told him that we hoped his technique would improve as a result.

Noel still phones Sheila from his home at a prearranged time once a month. She lies on the sofa playing with herself as they exchange sexy talk. I understand that they are trying for a mutual orgasm by phone. I usually take photos during these sessions, thinking of that special time in Rhodes.

David, Nottingham

Smut And Geoff

I would like to tell you about an experience I had a few months after my 26th birthday with a work mate of my husband. Kevin and I have been married for three years now, and a while ago we asked a mate of his, Geoff, to stay with us while he moved house.

One Friday evening Geoff came in early from work, as he was going away for the weekend, and dashed straight upstairs for a bath. A while later I went up to see if he wanted a meal before he left, and to find out what time he was leaving. The bathroom door was open and Geoff was not inside. I knocked on his bedroom door and went in to see him standing in the middle of the room, stark naked, drying his hair.

Instead of leaving, as I would normally have done, I just stood there staring at his body, which was nice and muscular, and at his cock, which seemed huge compared with my husband's. He made no attempt to cover himself up, but just stood there smiling at me.

Now my husband has often said that he would like to see me having sex with another man, but I had always refused. All his words of encouragement came back to me as I stood in the doorway, and I just walked into the room, knelt down and took Geoff's willie into my mouth.

I felt wonderful, as his penis began to swell between my lips. Then he pulled me gently to my feet and we kissed while he caressed my boobs, my bottom and then my fanny. Then he undressed me slowly. I couldn't believe it. I was naked with another man, and loving every minute of it.

By now I couldn't wait to get that lovely big cock inside me, so Geoff gently turned me round, bent me over and ever so slowly pushed his firm rod into me. It was delicious. If only Kevin had been there he'd have been amazed as I'm sure he'd never have believed I'd dare do such a thing.

We made love for ages in every position upstairs, and then downstairs. Finally Geoff was exhausted and I was filled with spunk. He got dressed, picked up his bags and left for the weekend.

I was still lying on the lounge floor, leaking come on the carpet, when Kevin arrived home from work. He was surprised to see me there and at first refused to believe me. Then he saw the white creamy mess inside and coming out of my fanny and couldn't get his clothes off fast enough. He licked my fanny clean and then made love to me like a man possessed. What a weekend we had!

Since then I've let him watch another friend of ours have sex with me and we both love it. The secret is not to do it too often, so that it is always exciting.

Jenny, Manchester

Pedallo Power

I am twenty eight and my wife, Julie, is twenty four. Last year we were on holiday in Corfu and a good deal of our time was spent on a very quiet beach a couple of miles from the hotel at which we were staying. We had found a good place to sunbathe beside a small beach bar, and having found no better spot, we used it regularly.

17

One day there was a very strong wind and although the sun was out we were almost the only people on the beach. We took our towels and looked for a good sheltered place — which we found between to pedallos which had been pulled clear of the water. After we had been sunbathing for about half an hour I noticed that a couple of men who rented the pedallos out were sitting on the sand some yards away admiring my wife's body, and, it seemed, her large breasts in particular.

I mentioned this to her, and she said they would take more interest if I wasn't there. 'I'll go for a walk if you want,' I said jokingly. 'I dare you,' she answered.

A couple of minutes later I was walking up the beach, and found a spot behind some straggly bushes from which I could watch what happened. The two men were still looking over at my wife, and glanced up the beach where I had walked.

The next thing that happened quite shocked me. Julie stood up and slipped her bikini bottom off and then lay down again with her legs well apart, giving both men a full view. The men stood up, looked round and then walked over to Julie and sat on one of the pedallos, looking down on her.

The taller of the two had a hard on showing through the flimsy material of his swimming trunks, and he began to talk to Julie. Then she reached up and rubbed her hand over his bulging cock. He dropped down to his knees and began to grope between her wide open legs.

Julie pushed his trunks off, and began to wank him furiously. By then the other man was stiff and he too dropped down beside my wife. The taller of the two pulled Julie up onto her knees and, moving behind her pushed his cock into her heaving fanny and started to fuck her. The other man moved towards her face and without hesitation she took his cock into her mouth. I was wanking myself silly, still watching out of sight.

I saw Julie's head stop pumping on the man's cock and then saw spunk dripping down from it as he emptied his balls into her mouth. As he pulled his cock from her mouth, the taller man withdrew and came around the front to put his cock into her mouth. Soon her head was pumping up and down again. Almost immediately he started to moan and run his fingers through Julie's hair, pulling her down harder on his cock.

Meanwhile his friend began to finger her, and as she came, spunk was shooting into her mouth again, and onto her tits.

Watching this from behind a bush, and wanking furiously, I had come three times. After the two men went away I walked down the beach the same way as I had left. Julie was just coming out of the water after a swim and we talked about what had happened. We both agreed that if the opportunity arose again we would take up the chance to repeat our adventure.

John, Coventry

Four Friends

I've been married to Louise for about five years now, and although we've often fooled around with our friends we'd never actually tried wife-swapping until a couple of months ago. The chance came when we went with another couple for a weekend in Sydney.

During lovemaking Louise and I had often fantasised about swapping with Robin and Maria. We knew that Rob fancied Lou: she'd felt his hardness several times when they had been dancing close at parties. I certainly lusted after Maria, a petite Chinese woman who seemed alternately saucy and shy. Maria was particularly coy about dress — while Lou often wears low cut and short dresses and loves men noticing her nipples and legs, Maria is always modestly and immaculately attired. Yet I suspected that beneath her Chinese coolness she liked to fuck and quite fancied me, so we were hopeful that something might develop.

As it happened it was Maria who got the ball rolling, whether intentionally or not I don't know. We were all in a good mood when we arrived at our hotel, and when the receptionist mistakenly paired Rob and Lou together, Maria grabbed me by the arm and claimed me as her husband, and we all went upstairs giggling.

No one quite knew who was joking and who was serious. Maria playfully led me into one room, and I noticed Rob squeezing Lou's bottom as he shepherded her into another. When we got inside I kissed Maria, and for the first time my lips met hers, rather than her cheek. She looked delectable in a white trouser suit, and was heavily perfumed. I was getting quite hard.

Suddenly she broke off, looking a little embarrassed. After a few moments silence, she suggested that we see what the others were up to next door, and so we took a couple of drinks from the fridge and went to join our spouses.

Rob came to answer the door, looking sheepish and dishevelled. Through the chink in the doorway I could see a red-faced Lou straightening her black satin dress on the bed. Maria seemed more amused than concerned and as we settled down to drinks and got merrier, she flirted outrageously.

Soon Rob and my wife were kissing, and I noticed his hand moving round to caress her large breasts. I was enjoying the feel of Maria's body pressed against me, when she suddenly asked Lou how she liked her new 'husband'. It was quite a turn on to see my wife stroke Rob's bulge and to hear her reply dreamily, 'I've yet to find out.'

Sensing the mood, Rob then asked me how I found my new 'wife'. As I replied by kissing Maria, Rob continued: 'because she's always fancied being fucked by you.' Visibly reddening, Maria rose from my knee and playfully slapped Rob, and then whispered something to my wife. In a trice they pinned him down, pulled his trousers to his knees and exposed his large cock. Maria then taunted her husband by ceremoniously unfastening Lou's dress, letting it fall away at the front and then slowly unfastening her lacy bra to reveal her full, creamy tits.

All the time she was languidly stroking and licking Lou's neck and breasts, deliberately teasing Rob who, it seems, had always lusted after my blonde wife's ample bosom. Lou was also getting very aroused, and soon broke away to offer herself to Rob's hungry lips.

Maria was by now quite hot for me, but this time Rob was intent on teasing her. It seemed that Maria was self conscious about her black hair, smallish bust and short legs. In fact, she looked stunning and her shyness made her look even more sexy. After some hesitation she removed her jacket, but would go no further unless I matched her item for item.

I began to take off my clothes, and was all eyes as she bashfully pulled her jumper over her head and then slipped out of her trousers. In a well fitting bra and briefs she knelt beside me, and after a long wet kiss she began to explore the bulge in my underpants. 'Mmmmm . . . it feels good,' she whispered and took my prick sensuously but firmly in her beautifully manicured hand. As I almost swooned under her ministrations, Rob laughed: 'Maria learned her trade as a night nurse wanking male patients for five dollars a shot,' he said.

Soon Maria was no longer the demure oriental lady, but a raven haired whore, greedily gobbling at my engorged cock. I wrestled with her bra clasp, and laid her plump titties with their dark nipples bare. I twisted round to examine beneath her pink panties. Her legs were indeed short, but incredibly sexy. I worked my way with my tongue from her red painted toenails along the inside of her plump thighs to the aromatic, silk encased mound.

At first she seemed to resist, but then with a sigh she raised her ample bottom while I peeled off her briefs. Her dark fuzzy patch soon gave way under the coaxing of my fingers to a resplendent slit, lips already swollen and slightly open, visibly aching for a penis.

I only licked her spicy nectar for a few seconds before she shuddered to her first orgasm. She then begged me to enter her properly, and tugged me by the prick to the bed. With her chubby legs splayed wide apart, her tight snatch sucked me in, inch by inch. We moved together in a glorious rhythm for a few minutes until the sight of Louise ecstatically impaled by Robin brought me to a shattering climax.

What a weekend it was. Maria was two people: sophisticated and cool in her formal Chinese gown in the hotel restaurant; but later in the evening greedily sucking my prick while being rooted by her husband. Louise was as bad, shamelessly presenting her red and swollen cunt, with Rob's come dribbling down her legs, for me to enter. When we arrived home the following night, we were all exhausted but exhilarated. We are now all planning a longer holiday together on the Gold Coast.

Steve, Australia

Loan Ranger
I intended to reply to the letter from your young reader who couldn't understand husbands allowing their wives to fuck with other men while looking on. However, A.J. of South London (Fiesta Vol. 17, No. 11) gave some reasons and I'd lke to add to his experienced views on this fascinating subject.

For over fifteen years I've thoroughly enjoyed 'lending' my shapely marriage partner to other, younger, men. Of course, as a young husband, to have let other men fuck my shy, wholesome and pretty bride would have been unthinkable. But years go by and the thought of it aroused me. While having sex I'd suggested she let young men do all kinds of 'dirty' things in bed, using the crudest language to describe what was happening to her, and this always turned her on tremendously to make us both come in shuddering fits of groaning. Then both our daughters married and left home, giving us more privacy, and I decided if the chance arose I'd be happy for her to try it out for real.

How to find someone trustworthy and attractive, as well as being a good stud is the *second* problem. The first is how to get a nice respectable wife to agree to put on a live show for you. My problem was solved by my sister's silver wedding, which we attended. A friend of her son's was there, an apprentice deck officer in the merchant navy, about eighteen and obviously intrigued by the cleavage and creamy breasts revealed by my wife's low-cut party dress. He danced with her frequently during the evening's boozy festivities and she told me he was ogling down her dress and getting quite worked up.

'I could feel his hard cock pressing into me,' she said, quite pleased with her effect on the lad, and no doubt, as she has a big thrusting cunt mound, she used it to good effect against him as they danced.

After in the bar, where I was volunteer barman, I invited him to our room later, hinting that I had a bottle of hard stuff and cans of beer stashed in the wardrobe. Well after midnight, in our bedroom on the top floor of my sister's Victorian brownstone house, even as I'd given him up, a knock came and Jim entered in his dressing gown, game for anything. With the rest of the guests sleeping off the party, we began one of our own. My wife got out of bed and, wearing only her silky nightdress, danced again with the lad, barefooted, while I crooned 'The Anniversary Waltz,' which had been requested of the pianist all evening. The pair had little room to glide so they cuddled up and just swayed together, enjoying their bodily contact until it was more or less only a standing-up 'knee-trembler' dry-rub they were torturing themselves with.

'For goodness sake fuck her, boy,' I ordered. 'She'll never be more ready for riding. . .' To my delight, she allowed Jim to lower her across the bed, her legs overhanging and feet on the floor. He got down before her, raising her nightie to reveal her lovely bushy cunt and its pouting lips. Obviously his year at sea had not been wasted, for he immediately began to lovingly kiss and suck on her prominent quim, making her stretch and sigh and mumble with pleasure.

I helped Jim while she was getting well licked out by pulling her nightie over her head. She opened her strong white thighs wide to allow his head access to her hairy split mound, lolling back naked as could be with big breasts heaving as she moaned and clutched at his ears.

This was my first at 'wife watching' and I can tell you it was the thrill of a lifetime. Like A.J. of South London, I stood watching and wanking as the pair before me moved into position, and with my wife's legs wrapped around Jim's waist, the virile young sailor got his prick deeply embedded up her juiced-up cunt and began to fuck her with heaving bare buttocks.

So far as I knew it was her first fuck with someone else and the excitement of the new and unexpected certainly acted as a strong aphrodisiac. I'd never seen anything like it as she arched her body, grunted, shuddered, groaned aloud and bucked against him as he shafted her energetically. She clutched him closer each thrust, crying out so loudly I thought our little game would awaken other people. Never very vocal, but now approaching an unstoppable climax, she begged and pleaded for her fucker to continue, shamelessly urging him to shove it right up her cunt, 'up to the balls,' and 'come in me, come, come . . . fill my insides with spunk . . . fuck me harder do . . . give me a baby . . .' My wife!

You greedy bitch, I thought. To think I'd worried about whether you'd fuck and here you are — can't get enough and begging for it. I was left with a handful of come and they rolled apart almost steaming with bodily heat, young Jim absolutely knackered but she smiling across at me and obviously thinking 'you next.' But of course I'd shot my bolt. This disappointment made my usually sweet and agreeable wife into a scornful witch, deriding me just as the wife of A.J. does for not being up to it, addressing me as 'old wanker,' and turning to the youth beside her with long deep kisses on his open mouth to taunt me further and bring him to a second erection to pleasure her hungry cunt.

Truly, again quoting A.J., it is delightfully painful and bitter sweet to be taunted so. I watched while she kissed him from the mouth down to his now limp prick, putting its head between her lips and sucking almost as contentedly as a baby suckling on a breast. Talking of breasts, while he was being so delightfully sucked, Jim was fondling her big boobs and was evidently perking up again. Before too long I was watching them fuck again, this time more slowly as they enjoyed each other's nakedness, Jim below with my randy woman kneeling over him and impaled on his prick. I could hear it squelch and see it slide up her cunt as she rose and fell over his thighs.

I can't speak for how other women might take to such an arrangement, but that night it was evident to me my wife was a natural for an official 'bit on the side' with me as spectator. It was dawn before Jim went off to his bed — despite his youth and keenness, hard put to keep up with her new appetite. It was obvious she enjoyed displaying her nakedness too, for in between bouts of fucking and sucking, she sat with us naked and flaunting herself. One example, the room was usually used for bed and breakfast paying guests and had its own *en suite* bathroom. When she went to the toilet, she left the door open and we saw her squatting to pee quite lewdly a few yards from where we sat drinking cans of beer. A memorable night and the first of many with young Jim as her fucker.

One boy in the forces she wrote really horny letters to after we'd given him a lift and he ended up sleeping with her that night. This lad enjoyed performing in front of me as much as she did and spent several long weekends with us, showing off his prowess. He liked her naked and finding this sweet, she went about the whole weekend in the nude, doing housework, cooking, watching telly. Of course, every time they passed, he'd reach for her and kissing and fondling would end up in a fuck wherever they were — on the fireside rug, with her at the sink, a 'table-ender' across the kitchen table; and once on a visit to the cinema with us, sitting between him and me, after playing with his prick she crouched down between us and sucked him off. Thankfully the cinema was almost empty on a rain-sodden night, and although I was highly aroused by her act, I was sitting in panic in case we were discovered.

So like A.J. I hope others will share their 'wife watching' or 'wife lending' experiences with Fiesta readers. In his letter he wonders what the accepted word for such a person is. I suggest it's 'masochist' but who cares! All in all it has enlivened the married life of my wife and myself. We get on happily, live ninety-nine per cent normal lives with family and friends, hold down good jobs, and enjoy our secret life when the chance occurs. Finally, my wife looks wonderfully attractive and slim for her age and she swears it is all the extra-marital harmless fucking she's enjoyed.

M.H., West Midlands

The Thirty-Eight Steps
Maybe this letter will serve as a reply to the one from P.H. in Holiday Special No. 6. However much one loves one's wife, sex (something very different to love) can still become boring after a while. P.H. is presumably young and sex to him is still fresh. To know that in the last few years my wife has had sex with over 30 men, and to have witnessed most of them myself, also taking part in threesomes, does nothing to lessen my love for her. It is pleasing to know that at 43 my wife is still desired by so many men. The ages of her lovers range from a 17-year-old youth to a 70-year-old grandfather, and have included 3 Americans, a German, a West Indian and a Chinese. I'll tell you how, what some might call our perversion, started.

We were holidaying in Devon a few years ago, having rented a country bungalow for 3 weeks. The day we arrived I went for a walk to have a look at the surrounding countryside. On my return I noticed a young man near the bungalow. His back was towards me and he seemed to be making funny convulsive movements. Drawing alongside him, but hidden by bushes, I was amused to see that he had his cock out and was wanking furiously. Then I saw the object of his lust. My naked wife was plainly visible through the window, drying herself after a bath. At first I was angry that he should be using her to gratify himself but when I saw the semen fly from his cock in several big spurts, I discovered I was also thrilled by it.

When I told Judy about it she was distinctly excited, which didn't altogether surprise me because my slender, dark haired wife has always been something of an exhibitionist.

A couple of days later, I noticed the youth near our bungalow again, presumably hoping for a repeat showing. Having an idea I suggested to Judy that she should give him a really good show by undressing near the window and then playing with herself. She was enthusiastic and so I went out by the back door to work my way silently to where I hoped to find the youth. Again his cock was out and he was wanking, which was hardly surprising. Judy was certainly giving him a good show. She was nude and lying on the bed, legs flung wide while she fingered herself. It was then that I had the idea of him fucking her. I was staggered initially, but the idea grew in my mind.

The youth nearly jumped out of his shoes when I spoke and with some difficulty pushed his cock back inside his jeans, his face crimson. I urged him to go in and fuck her, saying it was better than wanking. My own eagerness amazed me.

Entering the bungalow with him I was nervous, wondering how my wife would react. I needn't have worried because after the initial surprise of our entry she was game for anything, the fingering having brought her to a state of excitement.

His shyness vanished completely once he was in the room with the nude woman. While his fingers worked away busily between her wide flung legs, Judy was writhing and murmuring in obvious pleasure to feel the strange hand there. They were both plainly dying for it and after a questioning glance at me, Tommy shed his clothes rapidly and mounted her. There was a brief fumble before his bum was lowered. Judy moaned and I knew he was up her.

I wasn't surprised that he didn't last long and as soon as he rolled off I took his place, my cock slipping easily inside Judy's very wet cunt. I was pleased that he watched us making love. Afterwards I saw that Tommy was erect again and asked my wife if she wanted some more. She nodded, a lustful expression on her hot face. Murmuring that she wanted fucking from the rear, she got down on her hands and knees. I had always known my wife was a very sexy woman but I had never seen her as randy as this. I saw her reach back betweeen her thighs to hold the lips of her cunt open for Tommy to slide his cock in. My wife's face was pressed to the pillow so that her moans and cries of joy sounded muffled. Tommy held her thighs firmly and I watched closely, unable to take my eyes off his cock as it drilled in and out of her. Eventually it was over and they collapsed on the bed. (I have watched my wife fucked scores of times since but that first day remains the most memorable.)

I had found the experience a terrific turn on and suggested that Tommy, a local lad, should spend some time with us during the holiday. My wife demonstrated a randyness hitherto unknown as she eagerly fucked with Tommy several times a day, virtually every day. In fact he had her far more than I did during that time. We instructed him in the things she enjoys and he soon proved to be adept at cunnilingus, my camera catching the joyous expression on my wife's face when he brought her off with his tongue. I finished up with over 30 photos of them in action. The most exciting for me was to fuck Judy while

28

watching her sucking Tommy's cock, something we've repeated with more than a dozen men.

Not surprisingly, our sex life seemed rather dull after the holiday and so began the series of affairs which has led to 38 men having had the pleasure of fucking my wife so far.

Richard, Cambs.

Upstairs Downstairs

Jim and I are both 28 and we've been married for 9 years. Jim is a successful writer, and we live in a large house with over an acre of gardens and lawns. We employ a married couple in their early thirties, Lucy as cook and general duties, Tom as gardener and heavy jobs in the house. They have a flat on the premises.

Jim and I are both very highly sexed. He is fantastic in bed. He fucks me practically every night and when we feel randy 2 or 3 times, and we have wonderful oral sessions. We also like a bit on the side whenever we get the opportunity with someone we fancy, so I wasn't a bit surprised when I saw him take Lucy.

It was 11 in the morning. I had just had my bath and was walking along the landing when I saw a spare bedroom door partly open. Lucy was bending over making the bed and showing a lot of leg. Jim went up behind her and put his hand up her short dress. I saw her stiffen then relax and open her legs. I heard her murmur something and it wasn't a complaint. He pulled her knickers down to her knees, they fell to her ankles and she neatly stepped out of the, She turned to him and her face showed she was loving it.

Jim opened her blouse and lifted her loose bra, and her large tits were free. He started to kiss them. After a few moments he lifted her dress, showing her luscious white thighs, and her large cunt. I wondered how Jim would compare it with mine. He stroked her cunt, and I was getting amorous as I saw him put his finger inside.

Lucy unzipped him and took out his cock. She smiled when she looked at it. Jim has a magnificent cock.

She took the hem of her dress from him, the other hand holding his cock. She lay back on the bed, taking him with her, and placed his knob between the lips of her cunt, then arched her back and his knob was inside her. Jim started to fuck her. She wrapped her legs around him and he was giving her one of his slow fucks I love so much.

I felt someone behind me, and a large rough hand on my tits. I was naked under my dressing gown. I sensed it was Tom — he had been eyeing me a lot lately. I hadn't discouraged him. I fancied him and hoped he would make a pass.

He drew me into an adjoining room, it was a junk roon with a mattress on the floor. His hand roved over my tits — hardening my nipples — over my belly to my cunt. Watching Jim and Lucy had made me juicy, and like Lucy I opened my legs. I felt him unzip and take out his cock. We tripped and collapsed on to the mattress, and he was going to mount me.

I hate being fucked by someone wearing clothes. I whispered 'Undress Tom, I want to ride you.' In seconds he had his few clothes off and was lying on the mattress, his cock sticking out. It was big. Bigger than Jim's, and Jim has a fat 8″. This must be 9 or probably 10 inches, and he had an enormous knob.

I shrugged off my gown and straddled him, placing his huge knob in my cunt. I was sopping wet and eager to take him. I eased his cock in and not until all of it was in my sheath did I start to ride him.

I rode him slowly, making sure on each stroke the whole of his cock slid in and out of me like a piston. His eyes were closed and he had a wonderful look on his face as his hands fondled my tits. It was wonderful to feel his big virile cock in me. I had my first cum in a few minutes.

I kept riding him, and after about 20 minutes the climax came — it was beautiful. Both orgasms came together. He was raising himself to force his cock as his spunk spurted into me. My womb was opening and closing, accepting his seed and spraying cum on his cock. I sat down hard on his cock and enjoyed wave after wave of erotic energy passing through our bodies.

Afterwards I slid my legs down, lying on top of him, kissing his rough lips, our spunk dripping down his cock onto his balls. I said 'Tom that was beautfiul, you can fuck me again.' And so Tom and Lucy became our 'bit on the side'. Jim told me Lucy was a lovely fuck and very keen, so we take them to bed a couple of afternoons a week. I bet they will never leave. Lovely as Tom is, I still want Jim to suck and fuck me at night. He is still my favourite.

Katie, Dorset

Spreading The Marj

After eight years of marriage, I never thought that I would be a witness to my wife getting laid by another guy. You see, my wife was a virgin when we married, and she was always very conservative in her views towards sex. The most daring thing she had done was to pose nude for my instant camera in the privacy of our own bedroom.

But after having two babies in two years, her outlook on sex has changed. For instance, when out for a drink together she would comment on the looks and appearance of some guys, and has recently taken to adding things like 'I bet he has a big cock.'' At first she put it down to the drink, but later admitted that she had begun to wonder what other cocks looked like, and if they were any different to mine.

Anyway, let me tell you how Marjorie ended up getting fucked by an old pal of mine called Dirk.

Dirk and his wife parted about a year ago, after a long and hard marriage. Since then he has taken to going out on Saturday nights with Marj and me. This particular Saturday night we were all having a fantastic time dancing, and indeed drinking quite heavily. After Dirk and my wife came off the dance floor, Dirk went to fetch another round of drinks. Marj sat down and told me that she had felt Dirk's cock pressing into her while they were dancing, and from then on, every time a slow tune was played by the band it was Marj who grabbed Dirk for a dance. On the way home it was also Marj who invited Dirk back to our house for drinks.

Marj's mum had been baby-sitting for us, but she pushed off within about five minutes of us getting home. We all sat down with a drink, and I asked Marj if she thought it would wake the kids up if we played some records. She said not if we kept the volume down and put some smoochy ones on. I said she was only saying that because she wanted to dance with Dirk again and feel his cock pressing into her. Dirk just laughed and said he didn't realise she was getting so much pleasure out of the dancing.

Anyway, they both started dancing again, and I could see my wife pressing really hard into Dirk's crotch. After about the third track of the LP, Marjorie's hand came round to the front of Dirk's trousers and started to rub his bulge. Dirk looked over her shoulder at me, and although I could have spoken up and stopped them, I didn't. Instead I gave him a wink and told him to go ahead. The truth is I was bloody well turned on myself, and by now was fascinated to see just how far my wife was prepared to go.

As they danced, Dirk removed Marjorie's hand, opened his zip and put her hand inside. She pulled his cock free and played with it. He started to undo her blouse buttons and then to unhook her bra (she has very big tits). He pushed the clothes off her shoulders (she wears front fastened bras) and as her tits came free he stood back and looked at her — all the while still dancing. Marj looked at me and I just smiled back. I couldn't speak I was that excited.

She undid the button of Dirk's trousers and bent down

to take them off. As she knelt, her eyes reached the same level as Dirk's cock. It must have been a full minute before she finally took hold of it and lowered her mouth towards the tip.

God, I nearly came in my trousers as I sat and watched my wife sucking his cock and listening to the slurping noise as she moved her head up and down the length of him.

After a few minutes Dirk pulled away, but did not let her stand up. Instead he knelt down, and facing her started to kiss her while feeling her big tits. He undid her skirt and put his thumbs into the hem of skirt, tights and panties. He told her to stand up, and as she did so the whole lot came off. She stepped out of the clothes and lay down. She must have been crazy for Dirk's cock, because she opened as wide as she can go. Nothing was spoken as he climbed on her, but she let out a long low moan as he entered her, and although I know she is a good fuck, I cannot ever remember her moving her arse like that or telling me to fuck harder, as she did to Dirk.

He shot his load after only three or four minutes and rolled off her. But he got to his knees again and positioned himself by her head. It was hard to believe as she took his limp cock into her mouth and sucked him back to an erection. He pulled away again and told her to kneel on all fours. She must have guessed what he had in mind, as she shuffled over to me, unzipped me, took out my cock and lowered her head onto it. Dirk knelt behind her. As he entered, she lifted her head and arched her back. She lowered her mouth back over my cock just in time to take my load of spunk — God, I shot what seemed like gallons.

As Marj was nibbling my flaccid cock Dirk shot his second lot of come into her fanny and Marj shouted for him not to stop as she came too.

Later we sat down with a cup of coffee and discussed what had happened. Marj was pleased that she now knew what another man's cock felt like, and said that if she ever wanted to try it again, the three of us should get back together. Later that night we had the best fuck of our lives, and again in the morning.

I know some people will think that it is dangerous to fool around letting other men fuck your wife, but we all agreed to is, and although Marj loved every minute of it, she has promised that it won't happen again unless I am present at the time.

Mick, Belfast

Cum On Eileen

Terry and I have been best mates since we were twelve and in the first year at secondary school. Four years ago, when he married Eileen, I figured that would be the end. He'd become the restrained married type and Eileen — dowdy Eileen — would be the wedge which would force us apart.

It didn't work out that way, fortunately. I grew to like her and later realised how attractive she really was.

The time came when Terry's job was to take him to Belgium for a month. We discussed it and agreed that I would stay at their place and take Eileen in to work every day. On the night before he left we all got very merry, Eileen was all dressed up, or should I say down? She wore a low cut black dress, no bra and, I detected, was wearing stockings and suspenders. I was definitely quite aroused. Terry was pissed out of his mind and we carried him up to his bed, undressed him and left him snoring.

Eileen and I were having a little cuddle when she whispered to me 'Peter, I feel so randy.' My exploring hands were on her ample tits in a flash. She kissed me more passionately. Up went my hand above the stocking tops and on to a damp area of filmy nylon. The outline of her hot cunt was beautiful to feel.

'I'll have to go somewhere,' she nuzzled into my ear. 'Go into the lounge — I'll be back soon.' I couldn't believe my luck. A couple of minutes later she reappeared in her dressing gown. It fell open as she sat next to me, and I encountered her nakedness. My lips fed on her succulent brown nipples, and her thighs parted willingly.

Eileen began undressing me and I offered no resistance. Together, naked and exploring each other, we rolled to the floor. Eileen's plump cunt lips quivered as my hungry mouth brushed against her love box and teased at her erect clitoris. My ears could hardly believe it. Eileen was whispering 'Put it in, please Peter. Screw me. Please.' With that she guided my throbbing prick into her juiciness.

I clasped her full bottom, a cheek in each hand, her sturdy thighs wound around me and my balls slapped against soft, fleshy skin. Feeling my juices ready to spurt I was going to pull out, but she shook her head. 'Don't stop. It's safe. Please don't stop.' There were tears of joy in her eyes as I emptied in three gushing jerks. 'Leave it in Peter,' she gasped, and rolled on top. Taking one of my hands, she placed it so my middle finger made a ridge in the folds at the top of her cunt, and she rocked up and down, back and forth. Her luscious nipples tantalised my chest. She made and kept up the rhythm until I knew she was coming. I had to kiss her lips to stem her vocal delight.

Like two naughty children we crept to our separate beds. I felt really guilty as I drove Terry to the airport. After all, one doesn't normally fuck one's best mate's wife. Sitting in the car park, Terry asked Eileen if she could go and buy him a paper. When she had gone he turned to me and said 'Peter, promise me as a friend to look after Eileen. She needs a man to fulfill her wants. I love her, but I can't really satisfy her. Don't worry about making love to her while I'm away — she's told me how much she wants both of us.' I was completely taken aback. Eileen returned and we set off together for the gate. They kissed, cried and said goodbye.

Eileen and I drove back together in silence. When we

got back I made a pot of coffee. She called from upstairs 'Bring it up Peter, there's a darling.' She was lying on her bed, her hair loose, completely naked. 'I've rung your office and mine, and we're both off with "flu". Come to bed.' It was just turned two in the afternoon when I buried my prick between her eager cunt lips and revisited her exciting body. That afternoon we fucked in more positions than even I knew. Eileen was extremely inventive. She shared all her deepest secrets with me.

After dinner she promised me new delights. Licking fresh cream from hard nipples and sipping wine from her belly button were only starters. To have one's cock sucked clean of chocolate sauce was yet another delight to experience for the first time. I lost count of the number of times my juices spurted into her, and I fell asleep across her passion drained body.

We spent the second day almost entirely in the bedroom, only breaking off to eat sufficient to keep up strength. How long could we keep it going, I wondered. Eileen must have detected my doubts and said 'Tonight I'll treat you to something I've always wanted to do.' I couldn't guess what, and she wouldn't say.

Lying in the bath later, I languished in the foam. Eileen came and sat on the covered loo and started to shave off the hairs on her quim. 'No, don't help me — I can do it myself.' She was adamant. Unscrewing a large bottle, she covered her whole body with glistening oil. Her magnificent tits shimmered and her soft belly sparkled. My prick was aroused as she applied the oil to her pink, smooth cunt.

Back in the bedroom, dry and sitting up against the headboard, I watched as Eileen sat open legged on a towel, caressing and enjoying her own gorgeous body. Watching a woman wanking for my pleasure as well as hers made me ache with desire to fuck her. But no. She knew what she was doing. Producing a crude, red, knobbly vibrator, she stroked, buzzed and excited herself. All I could do was watch. The show carried on. Eileen kept up a constant flow of words, explaining her pleasure and ecstasy as she came, came and came again.

'I can keep on coming for hours, and I'm going to,' she said, and the vibrator became redundant, to be followed by other devices to stimulate her cunt and clit. Finally I begged her. 'Eileen, please fuck me.' Her eyes lit up. We joined together and drained each other dry.

The month flew by and Terry returned. In some ways I was thankful for the rest and returned home to my flat. But the very next weekend the three of us agreed to live together, and have done so ever since. Terry and I share Eileen, and she is faithful to us both. We're the very best of friends and, I hope, will remain so. To the world outside I merely lodge with them, but inside we are the happiest trio alive.

Peter, Cleveland

All Steamed Up

Jim and I have been married for three and a half years. We are both 28 years old and have no children. What I want to tell you about happened last year, when we were on holiday in Brighton. Towards the end of our week's holiday we found ourselves stuck for somewhere to go, as we seemed to have been to all the decent nightspots. I was looking through the local evening paper for something to do, when I noticed an advertisement for a new sauna proclaiming that that night would be a mixed session. I pointed this out to Jim as the only place we hadn't been to, and although a bit reluctant at first, he soon agreed to go there.

I had better explain at this point that Jim has always liked me to flaunt myself — wearing sexy clothes when we go out to clubs, showing plenty of leg and cleavage. He once admitted to me that the letters he liked most in Fiesta were those where wives flirted with other men in front of their husbands, and I have done this myself once

37

or twice when we have both been drunk.

We arrived at the sauna at about eight o'clock that evening and found the place almost empty. Jim and I both got stripped off in the communal changing rooms and made our way to the sauna. There were two men already in there when we went in, and their eyes nearly popped out of their heads when I took my towel off. Though I say so myself, I do have a good figure, with large 38" breasts.

I could see that Jim was aroused by the situation. After about five minutes he got up and went to have a shower, leaving me alone with the two men. Soon afterwards I joined him in the shower. I was right. He was rather turned on by the whole thing, and as we washed each other he told me he found it very arousing to see me naked with two strange men. To get him going even more, I told him that if he hadn't been there I would probably have let them fuck me. Before we got too carried away in the shower, I suggested to Jim that we tried the steam room. As we sat down on the steam room bench, I realised that we were not alone. One of the men from the sauna was in there too.

Jim didn't realise we had company, and started getting fruity with me. I was so randy by now that I didn't even care, and as Jim started to play with my tits, I began to wank his prick. Soon Jim was playing with my clit as well, and this sent me wild. Suddenly Jim gave out a moan and I felt his spunk trickle down my hand.

After Jim had got his breath back he left to get a shower. As soon as he had shut the door, I turned to the mystery man sitting at the end of the bench. He had already started wanking his erection. As I grabbed his cock he took hold of my tits, and within a few seconds his spunk was flying. Without saying a word I left him as his prick fell limp and joined Jim in the shower.

Half an hour or so later we were back in our hotel room, both naked and ready to jump into bed. Jim was already hard, and in seconds he was inside my gaping cunt. As he fucked me he asked me what I had done with

38

the bloke in the steam room after he went for his shower. So he had known we were not alone in there after all.

Joan, Glasgow

The Postman Always Comes Twice

I thought you might be interested in the following adventure. I am married and in my late thirties. My wife Jane is 36 and has been involved with a local drama group for a number of years. In a play that they produced last autumn, Jane had to play the part of an unfaithful wife and, at one point, she was partially undressed by her lover on stage. It was only her blouse and skirt that was to be taken off, but my wife wasn't very keen on that aspect of it at all. However, she went ahead with it, not liking to back out either.

I myself have never been particularly interested in drama but I usually went along on opening nights to support my wife, who I must say is quite an accomplished actress. When the undressing scene arrived, I was aware of some strange feelings stirring within me. I watched, hypnotised, as the man (a local butcher) removed my wife's blouse and skirt before taking her in his arms for a passionate kiss that brought the curtain down for the end of that act.

I sat in my seat during the interval, stunned by the erotic sensations that had been aroused in me by the sight of my scantily-clad wife in the arms of another man. I attended the play each evening for the rest of the week, amazed by the intensity of my excitement each time. Our sex life seemed to improve that week also.

I have always taken the letters in Fiesta where wives take lovers with their husbands' permission with a pinch of salt. However, by the time the play finished, I knew I wanted my wife having intercourse with another man.

As I expected, Jane was shocked when I mentioned it to her, but I continued to try and persuade her. Surprise,

surprise, when after a couple of weeks she agreed with a strong proviso that it must be discreet and with a man who was clean and attractive.

It was just before Christmas that I met the postman as I was leaving for the office. He was a student employed for the rush period around Christmas. That evening I asked my wife if she liked him. She immediately said yes and put up no opposition to the plan I laid out as a result.

The next morning I stood at the end of the drive watching for hime while Jane waited by a stepladder placed on the front porch. When I spotted him, I signalled to Jane and ducked behind some bushes. Jane, as planned, climbed the stepladder to fix some holly and other decorations above the door. I noticed that the postman visibly quickened his pace when he caught sight of her. He stopped at the foot of the ladder, looking upwards and I knew from our rehearsal that he would be able to see Jane's thighs above her stockings.

I heard Jane say 'I hope you're enjoying the view,' and his cheeky reply, 'It would be better if you were higher up.' 'Like this?' Jane asked climbing to the top step. 'Yes, I like your taste in knickers,' he said, and I was excited to realise how much he could see. Then, as my wife stepped down, I saw the postman run his hand up her leg to the top of her stocking. I knew at that moment that my plan would prove successful.

'Will you come in?' asked my wife and her voice sounded a little shaky. So they both disappeared inside. I gave them a few minutes before I stealthily entered the house. It was quiet downstairs so I knew they were already in the bedroom. He hadn't wasted any time. Peeping in carefully, I caught my breath when I saw the postman in the act of removing his pants and Jane, on the bed in her underwear, removing her stockings.

I didn't miss the way my wife stared at his penis. In fact, I experienced a twinge of jealousy when I saw that he was better endowed than me. As she removed her bra, Jane was eyeing the slim body of the postman with undisguised lust. Of course, he was in better shape than I was, and about 20 years younger too.

Then I witnessed something that set my pulse racing. Moving to stand in front of my wife, he whispered something to her. Seeing her rather shocked expression, I guessed what he wanted. While Jane hesitated, he leaned further forward, holding the back of her head and brushing her lips with his penis. Then I watched, spellbound, as my wife's reluctance and inhibitions seemed to fall away.

Pushing the postman's hand aside, she grasped his penis by the root and began to lick the glans. I saw a smile spread across his face as she really went to town. She licked up and down the shaft, all over his balls and finally took two or three inches of it into her mouth. I leaned backwards against the wall, trying to calm myself down a little.

Realising that the grunting had stopped, I peered round again and was just in time to see that he had pulled her knickers down. He was on his knees and it was obvious from my wife's squealing and wriggling that he was licking out her vagina. After a few moments, he really plunged his face between her thighs. Jane told me later that his tongue had bored right inside her vagina, and she had experienced an intense orgasm when he reached her clitoris.

I heard the postman say, 'Turn around, get down on your knees because I'm going to fuck you from behind,' 'Oh yes,' my wife gasped. Her face was flushed and her eyes shone with a look I had never seen before. Once she had obeyed him, he wasted no time in taking up his position. I watched closely as he guided his penis up between her thighs with one hand and with the other, opened her vagina. Then he slid it right in. Once he was fully embedded, he leaned forward to fondle her hanging breasts.

He began to ride her furiously, his buttocks jerking back and forth, his penis disappearing and reappearing behind Jane's writhing bottom. Her cries were building up and soon he too was grunting quite loudly. His thrusts became faster and then stopped suddenly. I realised he was emptying his semen inside my squealing wife. At that point, I left the house, my mind in a turmoil but excited beyond belief.

That evening we discussed the situation and my wife agreed, under pressure, that she had experienced more pleasure with the postman than with me. My initial jealousy soon subsided and I encouraged her to have intercourse with him again. I wasn't exactly surprised at her enthusiasm to comply. Now that he no longer delivers the mail, we have talked about another lover, if a suitable opportunity arises.

John P., Northants

Men At Work

A few months ago my sex-life was almost non-existent, so my husband, Brian, and I sat down to talk the problem over.

Brian is an avid reader of Fiesta and he suggested that we looked through a copy for some ideas to liven things up. There was a letter about a man who let his wife go to bed with other men, and although we didn't agree on anything at the time, it was obvious we both had the same idea.

My chance to make things happen came rather suddenly when two workmen arrived to mend the road outside our house.

I asked Brian to go upstairs for a while, and on the way he arranged the mirror on the landing so that he could see whatever was happening in the lounge downstairs.

A few minutes later I called the workmen in for a cup of tea. One of them was a lad of about 19, blond and thin, and the other was in his mid-twenties with dark curly hair.

They sat down and I made them a pot of tea, constantly

aware that they were watching my arse. I had to reach up to a shelf to get the sugar down and they got a good view of it then, naked as the day I was born.

I sat facing them as they drank their tea, my knees up on the sofa, and I could see they were getting a bit hot under the collar. As I stood up I let my kimono flap open wide, and I walked over to sit on the arm of the chair in between them.

The dark haired man turned and put his arm around me, pulling me towards him and kissing me. The other guy's hands were caressing my legs, working their way up towards my cunt. I was getting very wet and I could feel my sex juices running out of me. The first guy began to suck my tits and I slipped my hand down his trousers to feel his lovely big cock. Then I unzipped him and pulled it out from his pants.

The blond guy slipped his fingers into my wet fanny and began to frig me hard, wanking himself at the same time.

I slid the first guy's cock into my mouth and sucked hard on it, and as I did the blond guy pulled his fingers from me and put his lovely hot cock deep into me from behind. The harder he pumped, the harder I sucked, and we all came together, shuddering like an earthquake.

Then they laid me on the floor and they both fucked me again. When they had left, Brian came downstairs, his cock still out, limp from wanking hmself silly. So thanks to Fiesta we are happy again.

Mrs B., Middx.

Flash In The Van
My wife is a very shapely and attractive brunette, and I feel very excited and proud when I notice other men ogling her beauty. I became more and more excited on a shopping expedition last summer, when I noticed the number of men staring at her. I realised what they were seeing when I waited on a seat while she looked in a

brightly lit jeweller's window.

With the light shining through her summer dress, her shapely silhouette was clearly visible, even showing that she was wearing stockings. As she walked back to me, the breeze blew her button-through dress open, revealing a flash of thigh above her stockings.

After the shopping I drove to some local woods — notorious for voyeurs — in the hope of giving a show. I parked in the trees, and reclining the seats, began to kiss Ann and caress her body. I glanced up, and with mounting excitement saw some men approaching our car through the trees.

Unfastening Ann's dress, I slipped off her brief panties and put them on the seat behind me. As my fingers caressed her moist clit, I unbuttoned her dress completely, revealing her beautiful body, naked except for stockings and suspenders. Glancing quickly over my shoulder, I saw about five or six faces staring into the car, even leaning over the bonnet to stare through the window at Ann's wet cunt.

Ann was getting really roused now, as I stroked her naked breasts. I slid my hands down her body and slipped my fingers into her soaking fanny. I pushed her legs wide apart and parted her cunt lips so that the spectators had a good view, and as the car window was half open, the men could also hear Ann as she came to a noisy climax.

She was completely worked up now, arching her back and writhing her body with each noisy climax as I continued to finger her. Her hands unfastened my trousers and she began to play frantically with my prick. 'Fuck me,' she cried, but as my excitement was so great I felt myself coming. As I did, I leaned over her so that my spunk shot onto her fanny and pubic mound. After I had climaxed, I continued caressing her to yet another writhing orgasm, rubbing my spunk over her thighs, up her body and all over her beautiful tits.

The performance was now over, and I lay on top of her to give the men a chance to clear, as I knew Ann would not want to have exhibited herself. Unfortunately I have not yet been able to repeat this experience, as one of the men had obviously reached through the open window behind me, when we were beyond noticing, and taken Ann's little panties off the seat. When she could not find them, she guessed angrily at the reason.

I would like to ask the voyeurs out there to settle for the show and not get greedy. Otherwise it spoils things for all of us.

J.K., Midlands

Office Rocker

A few weeks ago, I walked unannounced into my husband's office, as his secretary was not at her desk in the ante-office. Imagine my reaction when I saw her sitting on his desk facing him with her skirt up round her waist and him fondling her suspenders and stocking tops while she pulled at his penis which was sticking out stiff from his unzipped flies.

They broke off when I entered and each tried to cover their guilt, but it was too late — I had seen everything. His secretary fled out of the door back to her room while he stood there, desperately trying to push his penis back into his trousers, then crying out as the zip caught his foreskin!

I couldn't find anything to say, I was so furious — and dashed out of the office, getting a taxi back home.

He got home about two in the morning and, as I had locked our bedroom door, he slept in the spare room that night. The following morning, he crept downstairs and was about to make a bolt for the front door, when I intercepted him. He was full of abject apologies and even went on his knees to beg my forgiveness. He said that he loved me passionately, but that his secretary dressed so excitingly she had got him worked up beyond control.

Whether that was meant as a hint I am not sure, but I took it as that and went out and spent a small fortune on

45

new feminine clothes, especially undies — bras, panties, French knickers, slips, petticoats, stockings and half a dozen assorted suspender belts, as I suspected that it was the stockings and suspenders that had really turned him on. How right I was!

That night, he returned home looking very sheepish, but his eyes opened when he saw that I had obviously made a big effort. I led him into the lounge and unfastened his trousers, letting them fall to the floor. Then I slid his underpants off and began to gently rub his penis to erection, with my other hand caressing his testicles. He gradually lowered himself to the floor and I stood over him so that he had a good view up my skirt. He let out a near shriek at the sight and pulled me down beside him, hoisting my skirt up to feast his eyes and his hands on my sheer dark brown seamed stockings, long pink suspenders and frothy pink and black panties.

In about forty seconds my dress was off, together with my lacy petticoat and equally lacy bra and panties. We rolled about on the floor as his hands played with my suspenders, and my lips worked hard on his masculinity. I brought him to a climax and it poured all over my neck and chin.

The first thing he does now when he gets home — usually about ten minutes before he is supposed to leave the office — is to whip up my skirt and feast his eyes and hands on the feminine delights underneath. I am off tights for good now, and he'll never need to look at another woman again.

Angela, Leeds

Spur Of The Moment
Some years ago, before we were married, my wife and I used to knock around with three other couples. We would go for drinks together, but except for the odd snog or sly grope, nothing unusual happened — until one particular night.

One of the couples' parents had gone away on holiday, so we all went back to their house after going to the pub. After a few more drinks, someone suggested we get a pack of cards, and whoever cut the highest could dare the lowest to do anything. As the drink took effect, the dares became more sexual, until eventually we were all in some state of undress. Indeed, my wife and another girl had actually removed their tights and panties and given us a quick flash.

It seemed inevitable that we pair off, and I found myself in a bedroom with somebody else's girl. I'm ashamed to admit that, after one quick jump, I fell asleep. My wife, Angela, woke me up in the early hours and said it was time we got a taxi home. We had a mile to walk to the taxi rank and on the way she told me what I had missed.

It seemed they had swapped partners again and again while I was asleep. Angela said she was very sore — which was not surprising as she had been fucked by each of the lads twice.

Afterwards, I said, jokingly, that for six jumps she could have earned about £30 in town.

I thought no more of my remark, till the next night when we met as arranged. I asked Angela what she wanted to do, and she suggested a drink in the town centre. After a few drinks, she asked me how prostitutes operated. I told her they apporached kerb-crawling cars, reached an agreement with the driver and went some-where quiet to perform. She asked me to show her where it all happened, so I did. We stood for a time on a corner by a telephone box watching the action, then Angela said, suddenly giggling, 'I could do that' — and before I could stop her she strode across the pavement to a passing car.

As I stood, not knowing what to do, she leaned into the open window, spoke to the driver for a few seconds, then opened the door and climbed in. I stood ther waiting for her, and as the thoughts of what she was doing went through my mind, I became more and more aroused.

About 25 minutes later, the car returned, stopped about

30 yards from me and Angela got out.

I expected her to come over to me, but instead she walked towards another car, spoke to the driver and got in. Again she was gone for about half an hour, but this time she did come back to me. She pulled two £5 notes from her pocket, and said, 'Not bad for an hour's work!'

We went to a nearby pub while she told me what had happened. I admitted I found it arousing and Angela said she had enjoyed it, and no matter what I said she intended doing it again.

We agreed on a routine where I would go out with the lads a couple of nights each week while Angela would 'go out with the girls'. Of course I knew that she was really on the game.

We have now been married four years. Angela still has her nights out, and sometimes tells me how many men she has been with, but I don't touch her money. As she is more highly sexed than me, it means she is satisfied, without any emotional involvement. Also, it is nice to have one's own personal whore as Angela tells me all about the men who have fucked her that night, as I myself give her a nice slow fuck.

Lucky Jim, Merseyside

French Leave
Recently, my wife and I went to Paris for a long weekend to celebrate our fifth wedding anniversary. We travelled out on the Friday afternoon, arriving at our hotel in the early evening. We decided to have an early night so we would be fresh in the morning to go sightseeing. However, we went to the bar for a 'nightcap' and got talking to another English guest. He told us he was 42, married with children, and visited Paris regularly on business. He offered to show us round in the morning so we accepted.

Saturday morning he was as good as his word and showed us many of the sights of Paris. He had an appointment in the afternoon, but offered to take us out to dinner in the evening. Just before he was due to leave us for lunch, and while my wife was in a shop, Maurice told me how beautiful he thought my wife was and that he quite fancied her. He then astounded me by asking if there was any chance of him making love to her.

I was shocked and disappointed by the fact that this man who had befriended us was only after my wife's body. I told him no. He apologised and said he hoped we could still be friends, and that we would still have dinner with him. I agreed and then said goodbye.

Over lunch I told my wife what had been said and her face lit up. She admitted she fancied him, but she said that she would not go to bed with him. After lunch I realised that I was feeling quite randy and so we both returned to our room and had a fantastic fuck. Afterwards we kept talking about Maurice, and it was obvious my wife was dying to take up his offer. In the end I agreed — providing I could be present and take pictures with our instant camera.

That evening we were both very tense as June put on her sexiest black underwear and a very revealing evening dress. The air was electric when we met Maurice in the bar. I think he guessed straight away what the score was, although he acted the perfect gentleman throughout dinner.

When my wife went to the toilet, I told him what we had decided and he agreed to my taking pictures. In the taxi back to the hotel I sat in the front, while my gorgeous wife was necking with this man we had known only a few hours. My prick was solid and just watching them cuddle and caress each other on the back seat nearly made me shoot my load.

In Maurice's room we had a few drinks and then I left to fetch the camera. The sight that greeted me on my return I shall remember for the rest of my life . . . My beautiful June, dressed only in her suspenders and stockings, was kneeling on the floor with Maurice's prick stuck in her mouth. She was sucking away furiously while Maurice stood there with his eyes closed.

I started clicking away with the camera. Maurice moved behind her and knelt down, my wife going down on all fours. Then for the first time in my life I saw another prick enter my wife's most intimate parts. He thrust in and out slowly, while June just moaned softly. He gradually built up his speed until he was sliding in and out like a piston engine in overdrive. My wife shuddered and moaned loudly and then Maurice's movements became jerky and he let out a loud gasp.

I stripped off like mad, and as his softening cock slid out, I rolled June onto her back and thrust myself into her hole. The feel of another man's spunk burning my cock end as I fucked my own wife was too much and I shot off instantly.

June just remained on the floor while we men had another drink. The sight of all that spunk flowing out of her soon had our pricks rising again and we both gave her another fantastic fucking each.

Maurice then asked if June could spend the night with him. The look in her eye was answer enough, so I collected my camera and the twenty photos I had taken and went back to my room alone.

Looking through the photos and thinking of my wife still getting her fill kept my prick hard well into the night, until I finally fell asleep, exhausted from wanking.

It was after 11 o'clock the following morning when June awoke me. I made her strip off and I licked and sucked at her pussy while she told me all that had happened after I'd left. She was quite explicit about how it felt to have another cock inside her and I felt incredibly humble as I licked her lover's spunk out of her fanny.

We spent the rest of our holiday sucking, fucking and talking about the experience. We have agreed never to try and recreate what happened, but if by chance the situation ever arises again then we shall make the most of it. In the meantime we have the photos and our memories to keep us happily fucking for a long time to come.

A.M., Yorkshire

Finding Out

Over the twenty years we have been married I have been convinced that my wife has had other men, but she always denied it whenever I asked her, even when I told her I didn't mind if she did.

There were a number of indications over the years which pointed that way, like the time she slipped away during a wedding we were attending and I saw her get into the back of some guy's car. I cold not get close enough to see what they were doing, but when she returned half an hour later she had a smug and satisfied look on her face.

She has, in the past, been up to an hour late getting home from work and her excuse has always been that she got caught chatting and the like. On her regular nights out with her girl friends she has always worn stockings, as she does not like tights she says, and they always go to the local places that have a reputation for women who have, as they put it, 'loose legs'.

Anyway, about six months ago she came home late after a night out, and her hair was messed up, her lipstick smudged and I caught sight of a large love-bite on her neck. After much questioning she finally admitted she had let somebody drive her home and they had parked on the way so that he could kiss her and mess around a bit. When I pressed her further she admitted that she had let him fuck her.

I had a massive hard-on as she told me, finally putting into words just what I had fantasised about her doing all those years. I think she expected me to hit the roof, but when I pressed for more details of all the other occasions she just gave in and was soon pouring out a whole history of the lovers she'd had since we'd been married.

Since then she has told me everything that happens on her nights out and she has also gone into great detail about those nights in the past. It has amazed me to find out some of the men she has been with and what some of them like to do.

I know one thing for sure and that is that I'm now as

randy as a 20-year-old again and I get a great kick out of fucking my wife when she has been out and knowing that I'm adding my spunk to some other guy's deep in her belly. She says she wishes she had told me earlier so we could have shared her secrets for much longer.

Mike, Cheshire

Birthday Treat

A few months ago it was my brother's birthday, so my wife, Denise, and I decided to take him out for a few drinks and a meal. While we were dining, Denise brought up the subject of fantasies, and being a bit tipsy she told Paul about one of ours, which was for him to screw her while I watched.

So, after the meal, Denise suggested going back to our house for more drinks. We started a game of strip poker, and soon lost any inhibitions we had as Denise quickly lost her top and bra, revealing her firm breasts with nipples more than excited.

Eventually we had all lost our clothes and were sitting there bollock naked, my brother and I both trying to hide throbbing hard pricks. I noticed Paul staring at Denise's soft blonde minge, his eyes gleaming with the thought of things to come.

All three of us headed off to the bedroom, pricks and tits in full swing. Paul and Denise sprawled on the bed and Paul soon had his eager mouth working on her breasts. She grabbed his throbbing prick. But Paul wasn't in the mood for too much foreplay and he pushed her onto her back and pushed his long hard prick into her, giving her every inch. He soon came with a satisfied stream of grunts.

I was excited as hell with the sight, and as soon as he rolled off her, I pushed two fingers into her now creamy cunt and fingered her to another orgasm while my tongue licked at her nipples.

Unable to wait any longer, I slipped my aching prick into her cunt and started to make love, slow to begin with, then as my sperm built up, I rammed in and out as hard as I could and released my sperm deep into her cunt.

Paul then entered her for a second time as soon as I rolled aside, this time turning her over and taking her from the rear as she knelt on all fours, pulling and grabbing at her swinging tits, the sound of his balls banging into her bottom, now wet with our juices, was like the slap of thunder.

As soon as he'd spunked into her again, she turned back to me. I was having a long slow wank as I watched her being fucked, but she grabbed my cock and took it into her mouth, sucking with noisy slurps. I came in a shattering climax, and she gobbled and licked all my spunk, not wanting to waste a drop of it.

With the smell of our sex in the air, the bedroom was heavy with the odour of cunt-juices and sperm and sweat.

In the morning, still sore from the night's hectic screwing. Denise said that she hadn't had such a fucking good time for years. But what a birthday for my brother — drinks, a good meal, and the wife!

Dave, Humberside

Secret Life

My wife, Gail, and I have been married for five years and have lived a fairly normal sort of home life together. Then, one evening a few moths ago, I found a bundle of sexy black underwear hidden in a bag, which in turn was hidden in an old suitcase we hadn't used for ages. There was a quarter-cup bra, tiny black pants, and a black suspender-belt with stockings to match.

I never realised that my wife even owned such things, and when I confronted her with them, she broke down and confessed to having led a double life. It turned out that last year she had an affair with a man called Terry, who had suggested she make a little pocket money by sleeping with various of his business associates and clients.

Gail, who I had always thought of as especially demure, even innocent, said she had become fantastically turned on by being a whore and she had come to crave these illicit sex sessions, sometimes with more than one man. She had worn the sexy underwear while she entertained while I was out at work.

To say that I was amazed at her confession would be an understatement. But what surprised me most was that I was immensely turned on by the idea of Gail pleasing other men in this way — so much so that I pleaded with her to let me watch her in action. Eventually she agreed, and I prepared the event by drilling a small spy-hole from the spare bedroom into our bedroom.

On the arranged day I was a bundle of nerves and excitement, though Gail was strangely aloof and self-assured. In the afternoon she went out to meet her client, wearing a smart dress over her stunning underwear.

I waited expectantly in the spare room, and an hour later she returned with a tall blond man and they went straight into the bedroom. It was incredible to watch Gail, my wife, with this man, and I saw a side of her I just never knew existed.

She was in complete control of the situation and had soon disrobed her client. Then she sexily wriggled out of her dress and deftly removed her bra and panties. Dressed just in her stockings and black suspender-belt, she knelt in front of the man and took his huge stiff cock into her pretty little mouth. She had soon sucked him to orgasm and she swallowed all his come (something she had never done with me) before leading him over to the bed.

She soon coaxed him erect again with her tongue, and then she was straddling him, bouncing up and down as he pulled and played with her stiff nipples. Then the man turned her over and began to screw her slowly from behind. She looked ravishing in her stockings and suspenders and was obviously enjoying it hugely and she came off noisily.

It was all too much for me and I came in my trousers before silently leaving the house for a cooling walk.

Later, Gail told me that her client had fucked her two more times and she'd made another £20. I told her how much I'd enjoyed watching her, and that night, for a special treat, she wanked me off while she wore her gear, telling me how marvellous the afternoon's screwing had been.

This is now a regular occurrence and I love being tossed off while she tells me all the outrageous things she's been up to.

J.T., London

Slide Show

I used to be very sceptical about husbands who fantasised about seeing their wives naked with other men. However, my wife and I went to Yugoslavia for our naturist holiday last year and I took several photos of her lying naked on the beach.

On a recent visit to my house, a friend, who has known my wife and I for years, suggested that I might like to show some slides. I showed a few of my 'straight' slides, then went on to show the ones I had taken on holiday, including the several shots of my wife's naked body.

In the darkened room I could see my friend having trouble with his erection in his tight jeans. Soon he had his cock out and was wanking off at the sight of my wife's large brown nipples and shapely bum.

It was quite a turn-on for me, and soon I was wanking furiously as I put on a slide of my wife lying on her back and showing off her lovely shapely figure, thighs and hairy mound. My friend said how he wished he could slip into her moist cunt, and soon we both came in gushes at the thought.

D.G., Coventry

2. I CONFESS . . .

Fuck Soup
Lecher's Choice
The Lady Had A Tramp
Up The Junction
I'm Randy, Fly Me
Window Dressing
Espana In The Works
Editing The Software
Psyche Hat-Tricks

God Speed, Good Steed!
A Hospital Adventure
Garden Rendezvous
Heavenly Bodies
Museum Pieces
Crying Wolf
Shower Sharing
Changing-Room Voyeur

Fuck Soup

Many years ago, I was working in East Anglia. It was my first job after leaving school and I was the newest recruit, my room, although quite spacious, was on the ground floor, while the others all lived upstairs.

One Friday evening, I thought I was all alone in the house, the others having gone home for the weekend. It was a cold, stormy night and I was bored by the television, so I decided to have a bath and an early night.

The bathroom was situated off the kitchen, which you had to pass through in order to reach it. This was inconvenient at times, but it didn't bother me on this occasion. I relaxed in the hot water, washing myself slowly, feeling the tensions float away, leaving me refreshed and glowing all over.

Imagine my surprise then, when I emeged from the bathroom wrapped only in a towel, to find Angie standing at the cooker in the kitchen. She was slight with mousey hair and possessed a figure which, although many men may have considered it too small, I had admired from afar from the first time I saw her. I say from afar, because I thought she had a regular boyfriend who was both older and a great deal bigger than I was. We both froze for a moment, me in my towel and Angie in a dark red dressing-gown. She had also thought the house to be empty except for herself.

'I'm making myself some soup,' she explained matter-of-factly. 'It's asparagus, would you like some?' I nodded, not because I particularly wanted any, I just couldn't think of anything else to do. She said she'd go and fetch another mug and I took this opportunity to go and pull on a shirt and a pair of jeans.

We decided to drink the soup in my room, as Angie said she had never seen it before and wondered what it was like inside. As the company had seen fit to provide me with only one chair, and not a very comfortable one at that, we perched side by side on the edge of my bed. The soup was far too hot to drink straight away, so while it was cooling we began talking, mainly about ourselves.

It wasn't long before Angie asked me if I had a girlfriend, and appeared astonished that I hadn't. The truth was, at eighteen I had never been out with a girl in my life, and I usually became distinctly nervous in the company of someone of the opposite sex. For some reason, which I couldn't work out then, Angie didn't have that effect on me at all.

She inched closer to me and ran a finger along my arm. 'I'm glad we're alone,' she said, 'it gives us a chance to get to know each other better. You're really quite shy, aren't you?' Before I could reply, she leant forward and kissed me on the lips.

I was trembling with nervous excitement by now, and somewhere, a voice was telling me to kiss her in return. As I did so, she kicked off her slippers and swung sideways until we were both lying full length on top of the bed. 'Kiss me again,' she murmured, as I came up for air, and threw her arms around me. I could feel her fingers pressing into the back of my neck, forcing our heads together.

I was dazed by this time and started fumbling with her dressing-gown, but I couldn't get the buttons undone, I was shaking so much. She squirmed away from me and stood up on the bed, undid her own buttons and shrugged the gown off her shoulders, letting it fall behind her. She was completely naked and I could do nothing but stare at her marvellous body. Her tits were beautiful, small and firm with dark nipples, and as my eyes travelled down across her flat belly, I saw between her legs a delicious bush of pale pubic hair.

'Your turn now,' she said, lying down again. I quickly undressed again to reveal my by now rampant tool. I had never before experienced such a feeling of urgency as I did then. She grabbed my prick and pulled me down beside her, rubbing her hand up and down the length of my shaft. I thought I was going to lose control and come all over her, but she stopped suddenly, placed one of my hands between her legs. 'Come on',' she whispered.

I pushed a finger inside her and began rubbing her clit while at the same time sucking her breasts, rubbing her nipples with my tongue. She writhed beneath me, one minute her hands clasped behind my back, the next searching for and rubbing my balls until she stiffened and cried out, 'Now, now, do it now.'

I withdrew my finger and plunged my cock deep inside her with frenzied strokes and almost immediately we came simultaneously, our sweat-soaked bodies utterly exhausted. Neither of us could move for a long time after. When we could, we did it all over again, but much slower and less savagely.

She stayed the night — the first of many we were to spend together in what became a beautiful, though secretive, relationship. We were always grateful to that mug of asparagus soup for bringing us together, and even now I cannot drink asparagus soup without thinking about that very first night I shared with Angie.

Graham, Kent

Lecher's Choice

I am a fifty-nine-year-old director of a large public company. Over the past ten years my sex life has dwindled somewhat until it consisted mainly of visits to strip shows, massage parlours and the like. I sneak a read of several men's magazines, because my wife would have a blue fit if she knew what I was up to. Apart from the occasional fling with a secretary, my sex life has been less than scintillating.

Last February, however, a very unusual experience began, and I would like to share it with your readers. My personal assistant, Sarah, had taken a year's leave to start her family, and the staff department asked me to select a replacement for her from a short-list of three applicants they had chosen. One of the applicants for the job — a girl called Pamela — immediately impressed me. She was quite stunning in appearance. Immaculately turned out, with her hair and make up perfect, she was a natural lecher's choice, and duly became my new PA. *(Not what I'd call professional recruitment criteria — Ed.)*

Over the following few weeks I learned that Pamela was married, aged 27, had a 42″ bust, 26″ waist and 38″ hips. (I got all these measurements from clothing tags in various items she wore to work and left lying around). When she was wearing low heeled shoes Pamela was a good couple of inches taller than I am. She soon proved to me that she was very efficient at her work, but came across as being very reserved, and I began to wonder whether my initial reaction had been appropriate after I discovered that several of the men in our offices had already made advances to her but had had no success.

One afternoon we attended a retirement 'do' for a retiring member of staff and we ended up having a meal together. For the first time Pamela and I had a real chat. She said she hoped that I was pleased with her work and told me that she hoped to become a permanent member of staff. I told her that I was well pleased with the standard of her efforts, but that I couldn't guarantee anything — and I assured her that I would put in a good word for her when the time came.

I asked her what she planned to do if there wasn't a long term job with our firm. She said she would probably go back to modelling, as she couldn't stand the idea of going back to being a typist again. Her CV had said nothing about modelling and I asked her what she meant. Pam laughed and told me that she had left it off the application form as she thought she would have had no chance of getting a job if she owned up to being a model.

I was intrigued and she told me that she had signed on with a modelling agency, completed a course but, due to her big tits (her words), had rarely been offered fashion work. Glamour modelling had been her bread and butter and it had all started with some topless shots for a promotion to do with a new car being launched. From there her topless work had grown to include calendars, and eventually she found she was enjoying working totally nude for a variety of photographers.

About three day's later Pam brought some men's magazines into work, together with some calendars and the like, and she made me promise not to tell anyone else before she showed them to me. She sat in my office with me as I flipped through her portfolio of photos, pointing out pictures of herself which she liked or disliked in such a matter of fact way that it was slightly off-putting.

There could be no doubt that Pam had a smashing figure — long legs, high breasts, and a luxurious growth of hair. Fantastic. I enthused something chronic and Pam was quite flushed by the time she left the office. The next day she brought in some of the photographs her husband had taken of her since she left the modelling world, and I was knocked out by her private collection.

In these photos she had put on some weight as compared to her glamour days and her figure and breasts were much fuller — and much the better — for the extra flesh. She explained to me that she preferred her fanny shaved as it was in these more recent pictures. My prick was rock hard, and I couldn't get Pam's adventures off my mind that evening.

The following days at work I saw Pam in a different light and often found that I had a hard-on from watching her stretch up to a shelf or move around the office. A couple of times she deliberately teased me, I'm sure, by leaving off her bra. One day I jokingly asked if she was going to sunbathe topless on the office roof. (I had heard a rumour that the maintenance man had caught two girls topless the previous summer, as they sun-bathed on the roof during their lunch hour). To my surprise she asked me if I was a 'Tit Man' or a 'Leg Man'. I had to reply that it didn't matter as she had both, and she looked very smug.

Then one day our conversation got round to her photo sessions with her husband, and during the chat I let slip that I would very much like to sit in on one of the sessions. Pam went very quiet and was obviously considering my request. I was on tenterhooks for days, wondering what her response would be.

About a week later she asked me if I'd been serious about sitting in. I nodded. She told me that she couldn't guarantee anything, but said that she had told her husband, Ian, that it was my birthday on Monday, that I was a bit low and that my wife was on holiday. He had suggested that the three of us had a meal out and Pamela told me that she would try and engineer the conversation round to photography if we went back to their place for a coffee at the end of the evening.

Monday evening finally came. I'd booked in to a restaurant and went there in a taxi to make sure that I wouldn't be driving home. I met Pam with Ian at the bar — and I was impressed by them individually and as a couple. Ian was a 6' 4" giant, very slim and quite jovial, and Pam looked tremendous. With her hair piled on top of her head, she looked about 6' 2". We had a pleasant meal and enjoyed a couple of drinks with it.

After the coffee we sat at the bar again, and after a while time began to drag a little. I said I'd better be going, and Ian looked at his watch and agreed that it was getting late. I said I'd call a cab, and Pam suggested that Ian should run me home. We got in their car and again Pam saved the day asking if I'd like to join them at their house for a nightcap. I could tell that Ian wasn't too keen.

When we got to their house we had coffee in the lounge and the conversation moved to the plans we were making for our respective holidays. Pam fetched a photo album of their holiday in Minorca and we thumbed through the pages together.

Some of the photos of Pam were topless shots, and I remarked that I thought that the standard of the photography was good. Ian perked up at this, and asked me if I was interested in photography. I told him that I didn't know much about it but loved some of the effects that could be produced using modern equipment.

Ian fetched another album of photos, which turned out to be full to bursting with shots of naked women. He explained that he loved photographing girls in the nude. I asked him how he got so many models — for the album contained more glamour shots than I had ever seen in one place before. Ian said that he paid some models, got some friends to pose for him and even used telephoto lenses on holiday trips to nudist resorts.

He then asked if I would like to see his studio — a spare bedroom which turned out to be bulging at the seams with all sorts of photographic equipment. I asked about lighting techniques and he asked Pam to sit down and then he arranged some lights and told me to look through a camera viewfinder at the various effects that were produced as he moved the floods around.

Ian then suggested that I should have a go at taking some photos of Pam — to which I readily agreed. 'Go and put something more interesting on for our friend,' he said to Pam, and she disappeared to their bedroom while Ian loaded his camera. When Pam returned to the studio I nearly fainted with surprise.

Pam was wearing a waspie-waisted little corset, and a pair of high-heeled shoes. Her panties and bra were see-through, and her breasts looked as if they would burst the straps of her bra at any moment.

Ian sat Pam on the studio chair and adjusted the lighting, then helped to take a few photos of her. Pam went into a posing routine, which had my mind in a total whirl — most of her chest and back were bare, and I could see the crack in her huge, smooth bum. Suddenly Ian said 'Well, there you go, that's it, what do you think?' I could hardly get my mouth to work. Pam got up, as if to go, and Ian stopped her and asked me if I wanted a few figure shots to finish with. I just nodded dumbly.

Ian said to Pam 'Just a few love, please,' and she tried to protest, saying 'Oh no . . . it's my boss — I shouldn't really.' I could tell that her objections were merely a show for Ian's benefit, however, as she had promised me I would see her nude if things went well with Ian.

Pam turned away, removed her bra, then sat in the chair and slipped out of her panties, stockings and suspender-belt. Her breasts were enormous and when she stood up I noticed that her fanny looked big — completely hairless.

It was a good job that the camera was mounted on a tripod, for my hands were shaking so much at this sight that I would never have been able to take a single shot. Pam began to go through a routine of provocative poses for the lens, and I was clicking away furiously with Ian saying to Pam 'Good, now breathe in . . . really stick them out for the camera on this one . . . good,' and so on.

All too soon Ian called a halt to the proceedings and Pam took me into the lounge and gave me a drink while Ian was packing his gear away. Standing in front of me, still naked, she shook her shoulders from side to side making her breasts bounce and wobble and said 'Well, what do you think of your P.A. now then sir?' All I could manage was 'Terrific.'

Eventually, I got a taxi home and hardly slept a wink at all that night, for I was going over and over the events of the evening in mind. The next day at work, Pam and I were both a bit subdued, but it wasn't long before we were back to talking about sexy photos and the like.

She showed me the shots I'd taken on that memorable evening, but unfortunately wouldn't let me keep a couple as souvenirs. Still, I can't complain too much. My old P.A. is back next month — but Pam has been told by the company that she can work permanently for us — so it's not yet certain which of the two girls I'll end up having as P.A.

I am glad I can share this experience with your readers — I couldn't tell my wife or friends about it. I suppose if it had happened to most of your readers they would have ended up screwing Pam rotten — well for me that remains just a dream. So far.

Peter, West Yorks

The Lady Had A Tramp

Having been an avid reader of your magazine for two years now, I find that the time has come for me to write to you about my favourite experience.

About three years ago I came home from work one night to find what I can only describe as an old tramp sleeping in my front porch. The smell that was coming off him made me gag, and although this may sound corny, somehow he looked rather sweet lying there. After trying to wake him up for a couple of minutes, I realised as he came to that he was rather drunk. By the way, his cock was poking out of his trousers, he was having an erotic dream.

One of my favourite pastimes is finishing myself off when I wake up in the middle of a sexy dream, and I began to feel strangely aroused. I took pity on the tramp when I managed to wake him, and he was soon sitting in a nice hot bath drinking a cup of strong black coffee while I tried to work out what to do with the rags he had just taken off.

When I finally went to see how he was getting on, I was surprised to find that he wasn't sitting in the bath, but to my horror, was lying on my bed slowly wanking a lovely slender tool of some seven inches in length. By this time I was soaking between the legs, and I was starting to fantasise what it would be like to get screwed by a dirty old tramp when he suddenly looked up and caught me standing in the doorway. To my delight he called me over, and I complied without hesitation. He asked me to gobble him off, and I began readily. Soon he was breathing heavily and I knew he was about to come. By this time my juices were running down my legs, really gushing.

I raised myself up onto his hot toby and rammed myself down. He screamed, I screamed, both of us in pain and pleasure as we came together in a thunderous climax. After a short rest and a couple of cigarettes during which time we talked, he told me his name was Brian and that he was really down on his luck after the business he was in went broke.

Anyway, to finish off my story, I'll tell you that we fucked, shagged, screwed, gobbled and sucked all that night and the rest of the next day as well. We are still together after three glorious years. To conclude, a thought for all you clean living people out there: 'Don't let sleeping tramps lie — clean them up and fuck 'em.'

Jean, Dundee

Up The Junction

I am one of your avid wankers and although I have read other mags I get far more wanks per page from Fiesta than from any competitors. Anyway, I would like to tell you about one of my experiences.

I was sitting on the train on the way down to Birmingham and there was only one other person, a girl, in my compartment. She was sitting opposite me, and when I looked in the window I could see her reflection. She was about 22 and very attractive — tall, well-shaped and with long blonde hair.

I kept looking at her, and then I noticed that she was doing the same to me. I thought to myself that I would love to get hold of her and give her a really good shagging, but I decided that I was one of those people that things like that never happened to.

After about 15 minutes of ogling, a healthy erection started to stir in my tight jeans. I thought that if I got up and she was looking she would be bound to see my bulge, and so up I got. She turned around as I was still getting up and gave me a nice friendly smile. Then she caught sight of my bulging pants and, embarrassed, she quickly turned and looked out of the window.

In a way I suppose you could say I was flashing, and the thought of her seeing my bulging penis almost made me cream my pants, and certainly made my dick throb. I went to the toilet, but couldn't go because of the hard-on I had. I just waited a few minutes and then returned to the carriage. I still had this massive hard-on, and as I walked down the aisle I could see that she was looking up. When her view was no longer obstructed by the seats her eyes went straight to my bulge. I turned my eyes away so that she thought I didn't know she was looking. Then I sat down and began to look at her in the window again.

I thought that would be the end of it, but about a minute later she took off her jumper and undid a few of the buttons of her shirt. I could see her low-cut bra clearly and her tits looked very inviting. I plucked up all my courage, got up and sat next to her, mumbling something about having a chat. While we went through the motions of small talk my eyes were glued to her tits, and hers to my bulge. It was obvious by this time that both of us were as horny as hell, and moving closer I put my hand on her heaving right breast. We automatically moved our heads together and began to kiss.

She unzipped my flies and took out my cock (with some difficulty, I might add) and my hand strayed up her skirt, inching up to her damp pussy as she opened her legs. Still kissing, I stroked and then rubbed her as she furiously started tossing me off. After a while I stopped her, because I didn't want to come yet, and I undid her bra and popped out her tits. The nipples were massive, and I began to suck on them savagely.

She was sitting back moaning as I chewed on those lovely nipples. I moved my hand down to her skirt fastener and off it came, revealing a pair of very damp silk panties which I removed straight away. Leaving one hand on her tit, I moved down to her sweaty pussy. My tongue darted over her pubic hair and down to her fanny lips. She slid down in her seat slightly, and I moved round to kneel between her legs and began eating her.

I parted her lips and sucked furiously and licked at her clit. She was moaning out loud, and when I blew up her and rubbed my hand across her pubic hair a hot gush of fluid came down over my face. Without waiting a second I put my hands behind her and, still kneeling, I pulled her down onto my throbbing penis.

I slipped into her very easily and, supporting her back with one hand, began to slide in and out of her. This was fantastic. I pumped at an ever increasing pace and then suddenly exploded my sperm into her. At this moment an old lady entered the compartment, mumbled about a buffet car, went bright red, did a swift about turn and left again. We looked at each other and burst out laughing.

After a while we both got dressed, and we chatted all the way to Birmingham. Both of us got off there, and we swapped phone numbers and disappeared into the night. I've not phoned her, because I am engaged. But I'm sure I will remember her and that night for as long as I live.

S.W., Yorks

I'm Randy, Fly Me

I would like to relate an experience that I had only read about, but which I never thought could happen to me. I work abroad a lot, and therefore travel by air. I was returning to the UK from South Africa in December 1980 on a jumbo jet. The plane was still half empty, and I had just begun to think that I would have plenty of room to stretch out when I noticed a rather attractive woman in her late thirties or early forties coming towards me, checking the seat numbers. When she drew level she smiled at me, and reached up to put her hand luggage in the overhead compartment. She had gorgeous legs encased in sheer tan nylons, and she was wearing high heeled shoes and a brown tweed suit with a cream silk blouse underneath. I was interested even more when she squeezed past me to the seat by the window, giving me a good look at her lovely shaped arse.

She settled down in her seat and crossed her legs, and I couldn't help looking at them. I tried settling myself as the plane took off, and I finally started to doze, only to be wakened later by a voice saying 'excuse me'. I let her squeeze past, and watched as she disappeared into one of the loos. When she came back we both ordered a drink and started to chat. Inevitably the conversation turned to sex.

She asked me if I thought the air hostesses were attractive. I said that the blonde one had nice legs, and added 'but actually you have a lovely pair of legs yourself.' I moved over to the middle seat and bought her another drink. She thanked me and asked me if I really thought she had nice legs. I said I did and put my hand on her knee.

When she didn't object I started to rub it slowly, letting my hand slide on to her thigh. She sighed and said 'oh God, that's soothing!' Slowly I ventured a bit higher, rucking up her skirt slightly, feeling the lovely smooth silkiness of her underskirt on my hand. My hand went further until I felt her skin and then a silky strap — she was wearing suspenders.

By now my cock was rock hard in my trousers, I told her, and she said that her panties were damp too. I said we had better stop it before someone saw us, but she said: 'I want it. I want to see your cock.' She suggested the loo. It was a bit small but she thought we could do it. I nodded and stood up, with my erection coming up to my belt. A few seconds after I got to the toilet she knocked on the door and I let her in. We kissed, her tongue nearly getting down my throat.

I undid her blouse and squeezed and fondled her tits through her red silky bra, her nipples jutting out through the soft material. I pulled her tits out over the top of the bra and managed to suck at the nipples for a few seconds. She had my prick out and was wanking it slowly. I started pulling her skirt up and pushed my hips forward so that my cock was nudging against her red silky underskirt.

She cottoned on to what I was doing and wrapped my cock in it. It was fantastic. As she wanked me I got my hands between her legs and rubbed her pussy through her panties, which were also red and lacey and very skimpy.

Then I got my fingers past them and on to her wet cunt, stuffing two fingers in and pushing them in and out. She gasped 'I want it now. Please. Fuck me!' I sat down on the loo and she straddled my legs, flicking my rock hard cock with the hem of her slip. Then with that and her skirt up round her waist, she impaled herself on my throbbing prick, moving up and down its length.

I stroked her suspendered thighs, then her tits, and then kissing and sucking them. Then she started coming and moaned in my ear 'Now, now. Spunk up me.' When she said that I couldn't hold on and let it sit spunking deep inside her fanny. She got off and started licking my cock clean. She put her knickers back on and we straightened our clothes in the confined space of the loo.

We fondled each other in the seats all night, skipping off for a fuck every so often. She wanted to try it on the seats with a blanket over us, but I was scared we would get caught. The last fuck was memorable in that we had had a few drinks, and my hand up her skirt feeling her tummy and suspender belt and stroking her black fanny hair made her need to have a piss.

I followed her to the loo, and as she lifted her skirt and slip I put my hand over her damp crotch for a last feel. She let go and wet herself, the stream running from her now completely sodden silk panties over my hand. She gasped 'now look what you've done, I'm coming too.' When she stopped peeing we fucked over the hand basin, with her fondling my balls with her silky underskirt.

She put her finger in my bumhole and I came, spurting deep inside her hairy fanny. Then we slept the remainder of the flight. We see each other frequently and make love in any situation when we can.

S.M., Ayrshire

Window Dressing

I have just finished reading Vol 16 No 3 and I would like to say I really enjoyed it, especially the photo set of Fiona — she is gorgeous. Two of the Readers Wives also really turned me on: Pauline of S. Yorks and Julie of London. I would love to bury my cock between Julie's huge tits. The husbands of those lovely ladies are very lucky men. I would also like to tell you of an experience I had some time ago.

It all began one evening as I was going to bed. I live alone and go to bed early most nights, but this particular night I went to bed at about 11.30. As I went to close my bedroom curtains I noticed the lady who lives in the flat opposite mine had left hers open and was getting ready for bed.

I had often seen her during the day getting her car out of the garage, and the look of her always caused an enormous bulge in the front of my trousers. She is tall, dark haired, slim and has a fantastic pair of tits. Take it from me, she is very nice. This particular evening I couldn't believe my luck. She was not 150 yards away as large as life and stark naked.

My cock began to harden immediately. Her tits were so full and round and stood out proudly from her chest. Her waist was slim and there was a lovely triangle of dark hair around her fanny. She slipped into a long nightie and got into bed and then her light went out. By now my prick was as hard as rock and throbbing like hell. I couldn't get the sight of her body out of my mind, and I had to wank myself off before I could get to sleep.

The following day I saw her getting her car out and she glanced at me and gave me a nice smile. As she pulled her garage door down her mini-skirt rose to reveal a skimpy pair of white panties. Once again my cock began to throb. That evening I waited up to see if I was going to get another strip show, and at exactly 11.30 she was there stripping.

I didn't see her the following morning, but she was there again that night. I watched her every night for a week, then one morning whilst she was getting the garage door open she called me over. I pulled my door down and went over to her. I said 'Good morning, off to work are you?' and she said she was. Then she said 'Thank you.' I said 'For what?' and she replied 'For standing in your window for the last week watching me.'

I was embarrassed and did not know what to say. She went on to say that she had seen me watching her for nearly a week, and it gave her pleasure to know that I was looking. She then asked if I liked what I saw, and I said that I did and that her body, dressed or undressed, was very lovely.

She asked me outright if I wanked each time I watched her. I said yes I did, and that I went to work most days with a hard-on after watching her get her car out. She smiled and handed me a pair of 10x50 binoculars which she said had used to belong to her ex-husband, and also her white panties in a bag. As she got into her car she said 'Same tonight. Use the binoculars and wear the panties.'

All that day I just couldn't get over her straightforward manner, and on the night I did as she asked. I moved a chair close to the window, removed my net curtain and left a gap in the draw curtains big enough to poke the binoculars through. I then stripped off and put on the white panties. The thought of my cock resting in a place that had been covering her fanny really aroused me, and my cock became hard immediately.

At exactly 11.30 her light came on and she came into the room. Without looking across at me she began to strip. She removed her blouse and bra to release those beautiful big tits. She slowly ran her hands over them and then lifted one up, bent her head down and began to lick her own nipple. She then removed her skirt under which she wore black panties, red suspender belt and black fishnet stockings. By now my cock was throbbing madly and I was trembling with excitement.

She then lay on the bed and stroked her cunt between the lips, her fingers pushing her panties right into her quim. She did this for several minutes before she removed her pants. Then she produced a large vibrator from under her pillow and pushed it right inside herself. She fucked herself frantically with it until she was going wild. Then she suddenly went rigid, let go of the vibrator and grabbed her tits. She was coming, and by the look of it she was coming with force.

She then removed the vibrator from her fanny and began to lick it in the way she would lick a cock. By now I was wanking like crazy and about to come off myself. I shot my hot sticky spunk into those white panties. It was as if she knew I had come because she walked to the window and closed the curtains as if there was no one there.

Next morning at the garage she asked me if I liked it and did I wank again. I said 'I loved it, and I filled your panties with spunk.' She thrust a bag into my hand and said 'Keep these as a memento.' After she had gone I looked in the bag and inside were her black panties, stained with her love juice.

I invited her over to my flat for a drink the following evening and she stayed all night. She is an expert at cocksucking and she loves to watch me wank. She bends down and catches my spunk in her mouth, or she rubs it into her large tits. Now we screw together regularly and I wouldn't change my neighbour for the world.

A.L.H., Birmingham

Espana in the Works

Last summer I had the most tremendously great Spanish holiday. At 31, I thought I'd be hard pushed to get my leg over even twice in the fortnight. But no. It was like a dream.

Travelling down through France on the coach, I sat next to a 34 year old divorcee from Liverpool called Doreen. She told me her life story, the sexy bits included, and during the night's drive let me feel her tits and even give her a long-awaited finger fuck. In return she wanked me off twice. I thought my luck was in, but it turned out she was booked into a different hotel. Just my luck, I thought. However, we arranged to meet there on the second night. Checking into my room on day one, at 2.30 p.m., I stepped onto the verandah, wearing my denim shorts, only to find two young women stretched out topless. The dark haired girl said 'Hi — just arrived?' I stuttered. 'Yes.'

'It's gear here,' she said, 'You'll love it, won't he Jean?' Jean, who was all of eighteen, just waved her hand and hardly even looked at me.

Introductions over, Sharon, the talkative one, commented on my sun-tan and I told her that working in my garden I had a good start. 'Look at me,' she said in her Geordie accent. 'I've still got white bits.' And what nice white tits she had, fit to cause my root to grow. Jean's tits were superb, tiny little brown knobs that glistened with oil.

I left them to go down to the beach. Never seen so much flesh. Bare tits and bits of fuzz sticking out from miniscule panties. I sensed that my prediction of two leg-overs would need revising.

After dinner I met up with Jean and Sharon and we bought each other drinks. They both had those long sleeve t-shirts on, and my dick was semi-hard. They invited me up to their room to drink some champagne. It transpired that Sharon was 20 years old, and obviously on heat. She sort of touched me a lot, and who was I to object?

I said I'd take their photos. Well, to my amazement they went into a huddle giggling. Sharon said 'Will you do some topless ones for us to keep?' And with that, off came their t-shirts. I took about half a dozen, then Sharon slipped off her skirt. 'Away Jean, you too.' Unabashed, Jean dropped hers. Two very sexy girls clad in see-through tiny panties, half pissed, getting ruder by the minute. My horn stood up like a tent-pole.

Jean told me to pose with Sharon. I put my hands around her waist. She put them on her full tits, and waggled her bum into my crotch. Jean next. This time I slid my hands into her panties. 'God, I'm nearly wetting myself,' she exploded, and shot off into the bathroom.

Sharon smiled. She slid her panties off and pulled me to her. My shorts were undone and her cool hand cupped my balls. I slid into her moist love box with consummate ease. Naturally, the bed started creaking. Jean emerged. 'You randy buggers,' she laughed. 'Hurry up, I'm all juiced up.' Sharon's wildness was fantastic. She squealed. 'I'm there, O God, I'm coming.'

I felt Jean's body behind me, and reaching behind my hand soon penetrated her thatch. Quickly followed by my prick. I thrashed away and tried to hold back, but couldn't. 'Don't stop.' She shouted. 'Don't stop.' I didn't and my lot shot into her. Hell, it was only day one, and only nine o'clock at that, and I'd reached my target.

We got dressed, laughing and giggling. I nicked Sharon's panties, so she decided to come out on the town with none on. Sitting in a cosy little bar about eleven o'clock, copping gorgeous feels of both girls' tits, I felt in heaven. Jean was nearly incoherent. She kept on saying things like, 'You've got such a lovely dick, hasn't he, Sharon? No, I really mean it. I'm not drunk. I know a nice dick when I feel it.' We managed to get her to bed, and went to my room.

We screwed and screwed till I was dry. Sharon came and came and even treated me to a solo performance of clitty rubbing that was very erotic. Finally she slinked off to bed.

I slept like a log until nearly noon. A note was on my table saying they were off on a two day trip and would see me later. The rest did me good.

At eight o'clock I kept my date with Doreen. By nine o'clock she'd sucked me off in her room and I'd ridden her to ecstasy.

We went for a walk on the beach in the dark warm air, and if you've never fucked a voluptuous woman on the shimmering shore line, doggy fashion, with her panting as your balls slap against a truly round white bum, you haven't lived.

Day two over and I was knackered. Day three I spent lazily letting the best strip-show parade before me, not even getting a hard-on. Would I be able to last out? No bother. In the disco just before midnight I danced with a German girl, who, I discovered, was staying at my hotel. The vibes were clear. Hilda (what a let down of a name) let me know she was ready for it. In fact when we were dancing, her tits, thighs and crotch were frequently in contact.

Walking back, we kissed deeply and I felt her firm jutting nipples and couldn't wait for the moment to arrive. Even in the lift I had a hand in her skirt and onto her silky crotch. When I did get past them, just inside her room, I discovered the silkiness wasn't just the panties. Underneath she possessed the smoothest hairless mot my fingers had ever stroked.

'Schön — ja,' she said. All I could manage was a pleasant 'Ja,' and I laid her on the bed. The desire to kiss her all over was too great. A kiss here, there, on her thigh, her belly. Hilda guided my eager lips to her smooth love tube. There was no mistaking what she wanted. She was like a tigress. Firm, supples, sleek, with a hot mouth that caressed my knob with such expertise that I had to tell her, 'I'll come if you don't stop!'

'Gut — I like you to come here.' She scratched the underside of my knob with her long nails and expertly directed my pathetic three thick blocks onto her stomach and coral tipped nipples. Did I give her a good tongue job! As she peaked, I could see Hilda massaging my juices on her full brown cones and my prick arose at the sight. I got on top of her. Her blonde hair, blue eyes were a picture. 'You must fock me gut. Ja!'

I fucked her like there was no tomorrow. She hauled me into the shower and let me soap her exquisite tanned body. Under the warm water, my hands explored her hairless cunt. Hilda's kisses didn't help. I had an erection like a stallion. She went down on me, I on her, she on me. Finally I knew she was not going to pull me out this time. Wham! I creamed off in her mouth. My first. I had to repay her. Crouched between her sturdy thighs, I tongued her clit till she was almost breathless. I know women don't shoot off, but Hilda's climaxes with warm water dribbling down us both gave the moment added pleasure. Sleep came easily.

In the morning Hilda wanted to fuck again, so we did. Over lunch Sharon and Jean turned up. They looked at Hilda and Sharon whispered, 'Is she hot?' My expression told everything. 'Not as good as two of us together. See you at eight,' and off they pranced.

Hilda took me to a quiet cove where we lay and felt each other. She wanted an underwater fuck, and we had fun trying to keep together. There was only one other couple in the cove and as we came out of the water they went and we were screwing like crazy. I made an excuse to Hilda that I had to go to see the courier that night, and used the couple of hours to sleep shower and shave in readiness for the Geordie lasses.

I was awakened from my drowsiness. They were sitting on my bed, their t-shirts, panties and shorts in a heap. Sharon's tits were at my lips and my hand crept up to her cunt, deliciously wet. Jean was slowly wanking my knob against her open crack, extolling the length and width of my prick. I felt it disappear inside her. By then Sharon had edged up the bed and I strained to get my face nestled into her cunt.

Both of them were chanting, 'Faster, faster, faster.' The perspiration poured off of me. Sharon came first and rolled over. Jean carried on bucking up and down, her tiny brown nipples sticking out with excitement. She came with a gasp of delight. Immediately Sharon took her place. All I had to do was lie there. She sure was fucking me. Somewhere from my hidden resources I managed to cream about the same time as Sharon.

My poor exhausted dick lay spent on my belly. 'Girls,' I said exhaustedly, 'Give me a break.' They were still full of energy. 'Go play with yourselves for a bit.' To my utter surprise, that's just what they did, while I had yet another shower. Eventually we went out to a nice Spanish bar to regain our strength. I got stoned and was put to bed in a mist.

On the fifth day I decided I must give it a rest, so I went to Barcelona and had an easy day. On the return journey I struck up conversation with a 44-year-old lady from Nuneaton. She exuded sex — big tits, cuddly body, the lot. We dined and drank, then went to her beautiful apartment overlooking the sea. I stood looking out, her bare tits heavy in my hands. Shirley, (that's her name) wanted me to talk dirty. She said her ex-husband had introduced her to it when they fucked. Standing there on the top floor balcony, Shirley's clothes strewn around and my shorts off, she sat down on a ledge, I stood and she licked me, her warm hands holding my bum.

'Tell me you'll fuck me when I've sucked you nearly there,' she said between mouthfuls. She went on to rolling my prick between her breasts. I opened her thighs, my proud knob was eagerly welcomed into her glistening quim. 'Keep your prick tight up, I want to feel you when you come.' Her superb body trembled as I pumped my tool at a steady, squelchy rate of knots. Shirley came.

She led me into her bedroom, shutters down, and commanded me to ride her big arse. She knelt on the bed, enormous dangling tits and furry cunt twitching for my greasy pole. 'Peter, fuck me silly,' she pleaded, and getting hold of my balls, literally used them to stuff my prick so deep I thought it would have hurt her, but no. The more I rammed it in, the more she wanted.

I needed to pee. Shirley leapt up and took me to the bath. She stood legs apart, held my now semi-hard prick, prised open her cunt lips and sprayed me with a warm clear stream of pee. When my stream started, hers stopped. She directed my jet onto her clit, holding open her big hairy twat with two fingers. 'That's beautiful Peter — I'm coming.'

She wanked herself and at the same time wanked me. She turned on the shower and my cream splattered on her. We dried and fell asleep.

Shirley cooked me a lovely breakfast. She wandered around totally naked, every now and then stopping to sit on my lap while I played with her big beauties and reamed her hot love box. Day six was spent on her balcony. I slipped out to my hotel that evening in order to pack.

I counted up: Doreen, Sharon, Jean, Hilda, Shirley. Lucky swine. I crept quietly onto the balcony and popped into the girls' room. Through the shutters I could see two bare Spanish arses, belting away on two sexy bodies. My prick was erect at the sight. I nipped over to Hilda's, but came away as I heard her being fucked by some German guy. By then I had the hots myself. Last night, no nookie?

I went down to the bar for a drink. Maybe, I thought, the second week in Blanes would make up for the night's abstinence, when to my delight, the courier, Ann came over. 'All alone?' she smiled. I nodded. 'No you're not — I'm with you.' She poured me a glass of champagne and said, 'I've been watching you with those Geordie girls. One of them told me you were ace.'

I couldn't believe my ears. Ann; so sophisticated in her red skirt and prim blouse. 'I'm naked you know. All I have to undo is two buttons and a zip. Are you game?' Boy, was I! I had a quick pull up of her skirt in the goods lift as Ann hurried me to her room and bared all.

It was a fuck never to be forgotten. Well, not really,

because when I arrived at Blanes, Ann was there. The second week was sheer bliss. Cunt, cunt and more cunt as Ann introduced me to five more randy couriers.

I'm going again next year, with my prick held high and a whole new lot of women to fuck.

Peter, Teeside

Editing The Software

My husband Rick bought one of those home computers a few months ago, and he's totally obsessed with it. I wish he paid me as much attention as he does that stupid machine! Last month we had a few friends round for a dinner party, and of course all the men ended up playing with the silly thing. Rick was showing Nigel how to load a tape and the other two husbands, Derek and Peter, were watching. We ladies were feeling neglected.

Suddenly Nigel pointed to the screen, where all the program names were coming up. 'That one looks interesting,' he said. So Rick duly loaded it in, and the name came up on the screen: 'Stripper'. I recognised the name and panicked. Before I could stop them they'd started the machine running, and up came a message in big red letters: *'BECKY PLEASE LIST ALL YOUR CLOTHES'*.

Naturally everyone's attention was now on me, and I had to explain that it was just a silly game Rick had written. I was red as a beetroot, and of course they wanted the details. So I told them. Every ten minutes it selected an item of clothing at random, and flashed up a message telling me to take it off. I was usually allowed to keep one garment at the end.

'Cor, let's have a go,' said Derek, and before I could say anything he had fed my more obvious clothes into the computer. 'Hang on,' I said, 'it's hardly fair if only I play.'

'Why don't all four of you have a go?' said Peter. We all looked at each other. 'But you'd all object to your wives

81

playing,' I said weakly. 'Not me,' said Peter, and the others agreed. I looked at Lynda, Nigel's wife and probably the most inhibited of the four of us; but before she could say anything Susan said 'I'm game if the others are — this party needs livening up.' Cathy was easily persuaded, and to my surprise Lynda nodded reluctantly after Peter had whispered in her ear. I could hardly back down on my own.

Rick said he could easily change the program to work on all four of us. While he did that, we nipped upstairs to prepare ourselves and to make sure we were all wearing the same things: skirt, blouse, half-slip, shoes and socks (it was all I had enough of to go round), bra and panties. Seven items in all.

The men had turned the lights down and put on some music, and the TV screen glowed blankly in the corner. 'About five minutes to the first round,' said Rick, and he explained that the machine would choose four garments each time, which need not belong to one of us. It would allow us to keep four items between us, but not necessarily one each. So some of us might end up with two or three items, and others with none.

Then there was a *bleep!*, which made me jump, and the message on the screen read:
BECKY: BLOUSE
CATHY: SOCKS
LYNDA: SLIP
BECKY: SLIP
(I've still got the computer print-out, and I'm copying from that).

I was a bit put out about losing two items when Susan lost none, but nobody would listen to my protests. So I slipped off my blouse and wriggled out of my slip. 'Let's hope it's Becky's bra next time,' said Derek, and I went bright red again because I'd just realised it might be.

We sat around chattering for a bit, but the tension was mounting. Another beep!, and the screen read:
LYNDA: SHOES

SUSAN: BRA
CATHY: SHOES
BECKY: PANTIES

Susan had a few awkward moments getting her bra off without undoing her blouse, and I was starting to feel very vulnerable.

The next round disposed of Susan's slip, Cathy's slip and panties, and Lynda's blouse. None of us was showing anything yet, but we were all in trouble. Susan had nothing under her blouse; Lynda and I were down to our bras on top; Cathy had nothing under her skirt and neither did I. We spent the next ten minutes dancing with the men, changing partners after each track. We all sensed that the next round would produce some excitement.

Beep! And now it read:
LYNDA: SKIRT
LYNDA: SOCKS
SUSAN: PANTIES
BECKY: SKIRT

Lynda unfastened her skirt and pulled off her socks, standing there in just bra and panties. Susan coyly stepped out of her panties: she'd now lost all her underwear, but still had her shoes, socks, skirt and blouse. Cathy hadn't lost any more. Everyone looked at me.

'The skirt, Becky,' said Rick.

'But I haven't anything on underneath.'

'I know. Take it off!' I felt very funny as I undid the zip, unbuttoned the waistband, and . . . let go. My skirt slid to the floor and I stepped out, trying my best to look dignified in just bra, shoes and socks. I felt very naked and very sexy, a feeling heightened because the other girls were still decently covered. I was a popular dancing partner for the next five minutes!

Round 5:
BECKY: SOCKS
CATHY: BLOUSE
CATHY: BRA
BECKY: BRA

Now Cathy was topless and I'd only got my shoes on. Susan had no underwear, and Lynda had only underwear. Susan was looking very smug, since with only one round to go she had a good chance of staying decent. Round six wiped the smile off her face though . . .

SUSAN: SKIRT
SUSAN: BLOUSE
BECKY: SHOES
LYNDA: PANTIES

I kicked my shoes off, now completely nude. Lynda nervously removed her panties: all she had left was her bra. Cathy had only her rather short skirt. Susan did a sexy little strip and ended up in shoes and pink ankle socks. We danced for a few minutes more, until no one could stand it any longer, and we dispersed in husband-wife pairs (all very proper!) to odd corners of the house.

We've never had a similar party since, although Rick has hinted about it once or twice. I'm not sure why it ever happened: but it does show what computers can do for your love-life!

Rebecca, Warwicks

Psyche Hat-Tricks

I read Fiesta regularly, and I read once in your 'I Confess' section about a woman who flashed herself to men. Well, I am an 18-year-old male, and I would like to tell you about how I have flashed to a girl who lives in a flat in our house.

We share the same bathroom, and one night, while I was running the water for my bath, I noticed the curtain had been pulled round the wardrobe. Jane was hiding in the enclosed space, peeping round the curtain watching me get ready for my bath. I realised this, and so undressed very slowly and made sure I had an erection on all the time.

Jane watched me carefully, and soon the excitement

became too much for her, and she started wanking herself. I knew because the curtain started to shake, and I could faintly hear her moaning. She wanked for about ten minutes until she came. Shortly afterwards I left the bathroom and went to my bedroom. I now always tell her when I am going to have a bath, so she can watch me.

Another time I noticed she was hiding under my bed. I slowly undressed and knelt on the floor, thrusting my cock forward so that she could see it from under the bed. She started to wank — I could hear her moaning — and my cock rose slowly as I heard her. This made her go mad. I could hear her finger squelching as it jerked up and down her cunt. As she wanked I lifted my cock up and down under the bed for her to see, as though I was about to come.

Another time I read there was going to be a film on TV about cocks and sex-changes. I made sure Jane was watching the right channel when I left the room to leave her on her own. I walked in while she was wanking and, to my surprise, she didn't stop but lay on the sofa completely naked, finger-fucking herself. She moaned and sighed for about five minutes while I sat next to her, watching. When she came she bucked up and down, as her juices trickled over the sofa. Before I could do anything she got up and left.

The next day she walked into my room as I was changing. She had probably timed it deliberately. She stood there, her eyes roving over my naked body, staring at my now erect cock. She immediately lifted her dress, pulled down her knickers and frantically fingered herself. I told her to lie down on the bed as she would be more comfortable. She did so and I quickly undressed her.

We went straight into a 69 position, her sucking my cock while I licked her cunt. I spunked up in her mouth and she sucked up every drop, while I licked up her warm, salty juice. I then lay on her and thrust my cock up her and sucked her huge nipples. She had recently had a baby, so naturally her tits were huge and full of milk. I drank as much of her milk as I could, and it was lovely.

I just lay on her and let her do all the work. Being somewhat bigger than me, she bucked me up and down on her. All the time she groaned in satisfaction. I felt her cunt contracting and spurting juice all over my inserted cock. Eventually she had an orgasm, and she sank on to the bed as I pumped spunk up her shaft until I was dry.

We lay cock-in-cunt for half an hour, for all of which time I kept an erection. I fell asleep on top of her, my head in her tits, a nipple in my mouth. When I woke I sucked at her tits and drank her milk. She put her hand around my bum. I released some spunk up her, which made her groan. I then took a mouthful of her milk and emptied it in her mouth. She drank it and then we snogged for about 15 minutes.

I felt around her mouth, with my tongue touching her tongue. She had orgasm after orgasm, releasing her juices over my cock. As we kissed I felt her tits. All this time we were having intercourse. I then pulled my cock out of her cunt and licked her wet clit. She sucked my cock clean and wanked it a little. It turned me on so much I rode her. I pumped my tool up and down her clit, making her buck up and down. She moaned and groaned very loudly.

As I fucked her I sucked her inviting nipples. After a few minutes we collapsed as I had a shattering orgasm at the same time as she had one. We then separated and she left for her bedroom. She no longer peeps on me, but we regularly have sex. The thing I love about her most is her huge big tits. They are 42″. You could get lost in them. Her nipples completely fill your mouth. I also love burying my face in her tits and gong to sleep. I'll never forget the first time we fucked, we spent the best part of an hour together.

J.K., Belfast

86

God Speed, Good Steed!

A few years ago I was working in Lincolnshire on a big gas-main job, and I was in the habit of watching a lady at a farmhouse sunbathing in the nude.

She was a tall woman with a very nice body. One day we were digging across the road, just past her house and I decided it was time for me to go and have a look to see if she was lying out in the sun. She was, but she had a man talking to her, so I had to clear off quickly.

I motored to Woodhall for a packet of cigs. I went into a small shop to buy my cigs and a very slim lady came in at the same time. As I looked at her, I noticed she was looking at my jeans. I then realised that I had half an erection on.

She started to chat to me and we left the shop and talked some more outside. She said she had first noticed my large hands and then looked a little lower down and told me: 'Red shoes, no draws. Big hands, big prick.'

We drove down a road, me following her, and turned down a lane past the police station. After about a mile or so, she turned off the road into a wood and drove among the trees and bushes. I parked my van behind, then walked around to her car. She was already removing her tights, etc. Her skirt was very short, a red mini with studs up the front, which she had already undone. I kissed her for a few minutes and she then told me we didn't have much time as her husband was waiting for the car. Her head went down to my zip. I asked her not to play with my tool for a few moments, because I would shoot off quickly if she did.

So she lay across the seat, putting her left leg over the back of the seat and pulled her right leg almost to the steering wheel. When I pulled my tool out she said: 'Please, fit this,' and gave me a French letter. When she saw my prick she just smiled and said: 'Nice one'. Most ladies say: 'No way'. You see, I am blessed with 10″.

'Please hurry up, or we will be late,' she told me. To my surprise, I slid right up her, with no trouble at all. After about twenty minutes of steady riding, I shot my lot. She asked me if she could give me a lollipop. Not really knowing what one was, I said yes. She then took my tool and placed her lips around it, making it nice and hard again, which is not normally the case. Usually it takes half an hour to rise hard again. She claimed to have had loads of men. One had a tool so big he had hurt her for a while. She claimed her steady lover had turned her over about an hour before I did. We met and screwed many, many times before our contact ended. I often think of her and would like her to know she was the best ride I've had.

H.M., Notts

A Hospital Adventure

I would like to tell you what happened to me in hospital in July last year.

I was in a ward with junior trainee nurses attending me. They had been out of initial training for about a month or so. Their ages would be 18 to 20. After a few days in hospital one of the nurses asked me it I would like a bath. I said I would. Two nurses assisted me to the bathroom. One ran the water and helped me to take my pyjamas off and the other was called away. I was helped into the water and given a flannel and soap.

I managed to wash my face and chest and the nurse then took the cloth to wash my back. She did so and I asked if she would mind washing my posterior and testicles as they hadn't been washed for a week. She said it was part of her job to assist patients and asked me to rest on my elbows and knees. She washed my posterior and then my testicles quite gently. I just never thought I would have an erection as I had been very ill, but I felt an electric tingle for a second or two in the knob of my penis and a slow swelling. I apologised to her, but she said it didn't bother her as it was purely a physical response to stimulation.

My penis was by then fully extended, hard and soapy.

In my elbows and knees position I slowly moved my hips until I built up a momentum. She never said a word but held my penis in a steady grip, not even sliding it up and down.

I moved faster and faster like a dog until I felt a tingling in the base of my penis and my testicles tightened up. My penis started to throb and I knew there was no return. I gave several loud moans and ejaculated in the water. My penis throbbed for a few seconds and quickly subsided. She calmly proceeded to strip my slack penis of any remaining sperm and washed it clean.

She then pushed the buzzer for the other nurse to come and help her and she let the bathwater run out.

The other nurse arrived and they sat me on a towel on the side of the bath and proceeded to dry me. When I stood up to have my anus and penis dried, the nurse who had just come in noticed that I was still dripping a few drops of sperm which she squeezed out on to the towel. She gave the other nurse a knowing look but didn't say a word. After I was dried, they put me into clean night attire and helped me back to bed.

I have been discharged from hospital but still attend an outpatients' clinic four days a week. I occasionally see my nurse at lunch there. We talk but she never mentions what happened that day, although she often has a half smile on her face when she listens to me. I know she has a boyfriend and I often wonder if she tells him what happens in hospital.

Les, Hants

Garden Rendezvous

While doing my housework one morning last summer I looked out of the upstairs window and saw my new neighbour sunbathing on his lawn in a very brief pair of shorts. He was rubbing plenty of sun-tan oil over his muscular body, which was already quite tanned.

His hands were wandering all over his body, and it wasn't long before he eased down his shorts to put some oil around his pubic area. I noticed that he was clean-shaven between the legs, and soon he was completely naked. I couldn't keep my eyes off his growing erection. I felt myself getting moist between the legs.

I went downstairs and knocked on the fence between the gardens and asked him if he would like to come in for a drink. It took a moment before he answered, but he said he would come round in a while.

We sat in the kitchen drinking our tea, him in his shorts and me in my housecoat. He told me that his name was Peter, aged 37 and divorced, and I told him that I was a widow aged 40. He told me that his wife had gone off with another chap, but for the time being he was happy enough where he lived, especially after living in a flat for some years. When his wife cleared off he had decided to buy the house and make a new start in a new place.

I welcomed him to the area, then said that if he didn't mind, I would like to join him sunbathing in his garden. He said that he'd like that very much.

I went upstairs and put on my bikini, my heart thumping in my chest, hoping too that it still fitted me. Then I went to join Peter in the garden. He said I looked absolutely lovely.

I took a blanket with me for us both to lie on, and it wasn't long before he began to put more sun-tan oil on his chest. I asked if I could help, and as I leaned over him he undid my bra strap. I grabbed his penis, laughing, and told him that that was a naughty thing to do. Then I began to work his foreskin up and down, and he was enjoying every minute of it — and so was I. But then he told me to stop because he was near to coming, so I suggested that instead of wasting it we went inside.

When we reached my bedroom, we both stripped off completely and lay on the bed. I kissed his chest, stomach and penis, then I took the whole length of his penis into my mouth and began to suck him. He soon came, and I had the lovely taste of his hot sperm in my mouth.

Some of it spilled out of my mouth onto his chest, so I just lay on top of him and let ur bodies get covered in it. I kissed him and let him taste his own juices, and I swallowed the rest, which I thought tasted lovely.

But I wanted the real thing, I was on heat and I needed a good fuck. So I lay on my back and opened my legs. Peter climbed on top of me and began to screw me. It was the first time I'd been fucked for several years and I was enjoying every minute of it.

For the rest of the day we stopped in, not even bothering to get dressed, even watching TV in the nude before we went back to bed together that evening.

I discovered soon afterwards that I was pregnant. Peter was thrilled and he had no hesitation about moving in with me and we don't give a sod about what the neighbours think. They may even have seen us sunbathing naked together in the garden, but what goes on indoors is our secret. We hope to get married soon, and then the tongues'll wag!

Margaret, Birmingham

Heavenly Bodies

I love your readers' letters, I adore the variety of subjects they cover. I am looking forward to seeing my letter in Fiesta, as it's the first time I've had something to write about, it's the first time I've been fucked and now my virginity has gone! Thanks to a guy called Alan.

I'm 18 years old, with long flowing brown hair, brown eyes and, for 5ft 6in, I'm proud of my 38-24-36 figure. My hobby is stargazing and I have been at it since I was 11 and this hobby led me to the loss of my maidenhead.

Six months ago I made my way to an open field to a spot where I could watch Jupiter and Saturn in Virgo, away from the city lights. It was a clear night and I was well wrapped-up ready to spend the evening and some of the early morning stargazing (so I thought). The evening was quite warm for April and I had taken off some of my clothes, not knowing I was being watched.

Alan came out from the shadows holding a pair of binoculars. When I saw his array of star badges I knew I was facing a stargazer like myself. He was bearded and seemed quite nice, when he said, 'The Virgin holds two planets.'

I replied, 'Yes, Jupiter and Saturn.'

Being a virgin, and knowing the planets were in Virgo, and I being born in Virgo my star sign. It crossed my mind that Alan was the chosen one to take my virginity. I found myself saying 'How would you like to hold a planet? I'm Venus.'

He smiled and replied: 'May I take a picture of Venus, without her clothes on?'

Well I stripped at that moment and I could see him doing the same. We looked at each other and Alan said, 'Would Venus like a penis?'

As he came closer I could see his erect prick, and all that dark hair, even his legs had lots of hair, with his beard he looked so damn sexy. (I love men with lots of hair). I could see that his gaze was fixed on my firm breasts, as my nipples stood up and out like never before, and they seemed to tingle, as a fire began to glow within my belly, making my pussy ache with pleasure which is hard to put in words, because I've never felt the way I felt that night.

He stood over me, his hard prick jutting out of his hairy balls hanging heavy, filled with milk from the milky way. I couldn't help but say, 'I can see Uranus!' He sank to his knees and before I knew it I had his rocket in my mouth, and found myself sucking at it like a starving piglet. With my mouth full I couldn't say much, but could hear Alan mutter something about a meteor and told me to make a wish!

Alan knew what I had wished for. Before his mouth was on my tingling pussy, I heard him say, 'that's the first black hole I've seen with hair round it', I thought it was quite romantic. I have looked at the stars thousands of times, I just wonder what the stars can see from out there, me and Alan doing a 69!

My mouth soon filled up with milky fluid which I drank and swallowed greedily. Plop! Out it came, all wet and it looked even bigger. I was so worked up I felt like a wanton Lolita. I just couldn't help what I was shouting — Venus wants that penis! — over and over until that hairy shuttle entered my inner atmosphere. I lifted my bum to welcome the shuttle as it pumped away like mad. Soon I felt the shuttle shatter my virginity, then I let out a highly delightful scream, as the shuttle thrust in and out, in and out, going faster and faster, I soon came to such a climax I have never ever had before. (I masturbate a lot, using my own fingers that's all).

I could feel the shuttle spitting hot fluid into my now soggy hole. As its engines roared and groaned spilling its milky liquid in spurts, until its body came to a halt, and the shuttle wilted, due to its loss of life fluid, shrivelled up and dripping. I looked up at Alan who was exhausted, and said, 'What about a re-entry?'

We made love under the stars most of that April night, we had lift-off four times, and I was in orbit with the shuttle. While Alan explored Venus!

Alan, I know you read Fiesta all the time, it was you who got me reading this splendid mag; this is to let you know that I want to see that shuttle go up again. . .

Kate, Berks.

Museum Pieces

I came across your fine magazine about six months ago. A colleague of mine said I would enjoy looking at it — and I did! I work in a museum, so you even have some admirers in the academic world.

I have worked as a book stacker for the past fifteen years, and I must say, being 50-years-old, I still prefer the girls who are just around the 20 mark. I can afford to give those oldies a miss, but I'm all eyes for those 'sweet seventeen' faces and figures, they really make my lower half hum!

At the rear of all those bookshelves in the museum, are long iron stairs and corridors through which one can look up to see those working above. I like looking through the fine grill. We also have lots of spiral staircases, and when I first started work there the mini-skirt was the in-fashion among the many female staff. 'It'll put lead in your pencil to find out who wears 'em and who doesn't,' my friend told me. And believe me, he was right.

'I'll show you how to have a hard time,' he said. 'Follow me.'

Smiling broadly he followed behind one of the most attractive girls I'd seen in a long time. She had lovely long black hair which fell almost to her waist, and small well-proportioned legs which moved rhythmically with the clip-clop of her high-heeled shoes.

She turned right and went through some swing-doors. We followed hot on her tracks and when we entered the room she wa already climbing up the spiral staircase.

'Er, Jane, can I introduce a new member of the staff?' said my friend.

'Oh, hello,' said the girl, stopping on the stairs, her feet about level with our faces. I could see her knickers were of the flimsiest kind. 'Pleased to met you. Oh, and while you're here, can you bring those small volumes with you and I'll show you where to put them.'

I nearly dropped the books as she began to ascend the stairs again, her lovely bottom and stocking-tops appearing in full view. My penis was quite tight by this time and I had a wonderful feeling that I would shoot in my trousers as I followed her round and round and upwards.

I kept my head low so that I could see the lovely gyrations of her full thighs as she ascended. Suddenly she stopped at the top of the stairs.

'I wish people wouldn't leave books on the stairs,' she

said petulantly, bending forward to pick it up and revealing the tantalising zones of maidenhood. Lovely little hairs were poking our from the tight shape of her crutch, her knickers had almost retreated into her womanly crevice.

She noticed my hot eyes and quickly straightened up, pulling her mini-skirt down as far as she could. She was blushing, and this made me have my secret orgasm at last. It was a really beautiful moment.

'These stairs are difficult sometimes,' she confided.

My friend winked at me. 'Isn't she a looker?' he exclaimed.

I had to agree. Since then I have thoroughly enjoyed my fifteen years of following young girls around the museum — and particularly up the spiral stairs!

Bill, London

Crying Wolf

One cold afternoon I was walking along Kensington High Street after having paid a visit to the Job Centre. Looking behind, I noticed a girl who had been in there the same time as me, but at the time I didn't think anything of it.

It began to rain, so I retreated into a cafe for a coffee. No sooner had I sat down with it when the girl came in, got herself a hot drink and sat down at my table. My first thought was that she was a bit crazy. She never said a word. Then, when I was just about to leave, she began to cry.

I didn't know quite what to do or say. 'Are you okay? Can I help you at all?' I asked her.

'Will you take me home?' she asked, and as I'd offered to help her, then I felt obliged.

It was ten minutes walk away and when we arrived at her small flat she invited me in for a coffee and an explanation. She was about 27, with long blonde hair, ocean-green eyes and a lovely figure with long legs.

We drank our coffee, but still she made no explanation. Suddenly she walked out of the room without saying a word. I sat there stirring my coffee, and two minutes later she came back — stark naked! She walked up to me and began kissing me, then she grabbed my hand and pulled me into the bedrom.

She lay on the bed with her legs wide open, not a single hair on her sex. I sat beside her and started to run my tongue up and down her lovely body. God! Her sex was so beautiful, my tongue was in and out of her like a bullet.

Then she started to undress me. I'm not very big where it counts, but what I saw when she took my underpants off amazed me. It was much bigger than usual — perhaps because one of my favourite fantasies is having a shaved pussy to lick.

She bent and started to give me a really good going over with her mouth, and after a few minutes I had to pull away from her as I was almost coming. We got into the 69 position. By now her hole was dribbling, partly from me, but mainly from her juices. As she climaxed her juices started to run like pee. I have never seen anything like it in my life. I just sat there and watched the bedclothes get wet with sticky fluid.

After I'd got over the initial shock, we started to suck and blow each other again and I stayed with her for a few more hours before we showered and I left.

I never did find out why she'd been crying. Maybe it was just her way of getting a man's attention. I'll never know.

Keith, London

Shower Sharing
Some time ago I had to go on a week's course for my Government Department. We were sent from offices all over the south of England to a hotel in Hastings. There were six men and five girls, all aged between 20 and 30.

We all had to share a room with one other person. The one I shared had a loo, but no shower, and it turned out that none of the men's rooms had a bath or a shower. When it was mentioned, one of the girls said that if anyone wanted a shower they were welcome to use her room.

Well, a week would be rather a long time to go without a shower, so on the second night I asked the girl, Sue, if it would be okay for me to have a shower that night. She said I could, at any time I chose.

So I went there at about 8 o'clock and went straight to the shower room. I was having a luxurious soak, when there was a tap on the door. Sue called out to ask if I had a towel, and when I said I had, she asked if it wouldn't be nicer for her to towel me dry. It wasn't exactly what I had expected, but with rising excitement — and a rising of somethig else — I told her to come in.

She had changed into a very see-through negligee. She started to rub me all over as I stepped out of the shower, and before I could say a thing she grasped my throbbing prick and started to wank me gently. By this time I had grabbed two handfuls of very nice soft tits and was pulling at the nipples as they extended.

Sue then said she had some baby lotion and that she was going to rub some into my cock. She got two palm-fulls and began working it into my burning organ. I pulled aside her negligee and pushed two fingers up her hot juicy cunt, really starting to work her up as she kept going at my prick — which by then felt as if it were about to explode.

I couldn't stand it anymore, and with several exclamations from both of us, I erupted all down her front, all over her tits, so that it dribbled down into her thick bush. She, for her part, had a fantastic orgasm, after which we both had a much needed shower.

Needless to say, I went back for a shower every evening after that and got a rub down and more every time. So now you know what your taxes help to subsidise.

A.B., Wilts.

Changing-Room Voyeur

I have never considered myself to be a voyeur, but I recently experienced a scene that really gave me the hots. It was at our local rugby club dance, and as you can imagine, there were some lovely girls there with all those rugby-types.

One girl, named Carla, I couldn't take my eyes off. She was blonde and curvaceous and wore a low-cut dress which finished at knee-level. What really got me going was the slit up the side — and she was wearing sheer seamed nylons and black high-heeled court shoes. All the boys were looking at her, and every time she moved, the slit in her skirt opened to reveal a tantalising glimpse of dark stocking-top.

I love stockings, especially with seams — as most men do — and I was following her and her guy — a big-handsome prop forward — hoping for a flash of the old stocking-tops.

As the evening wore on I felt thirsty, and as I'd already had enough booze I went through to the men's locker room and into the wash-room where I had a drink of cold water. I was about to leave when I heard the locker room door open and the sound of voices.

I peered round the door — and there was Carla in her black dress with her boyfriend. They didn't know I was there, and they began kissing and fondling each other and it wasn't long before he was groping her tits. Then he buried one hand up her skirt. They were whispering and giggling, but I couldn't hear what they were saying.

Suddenly the boyfriend lay down on one of the long benches and ran his hand up and down the girl's legs, trying to look under skirt as she stood over him. Then she laughed and reached down to lift the front of her dress for him. Unfortunately she had her back to me, but as her dress was raised, more and more of those beautifully straight stocking seams came into view, then her stocking-tops and the clasps of her black suspenders. She was giving her boyfriend a teasing display of stocking-tops and

98

suspenders — and I was rubbing my rapidly stiffening prick through my trousers.

Suddenly she whipped off her tiny black panties and slowly opened her gorgeous stockinged legs. I heard her boyfriend gasp as her legs spread wider to give him a great view of her cunt. Her hand was between her legs and she was gently frigging herself.

Her boyfriend had now unzipped and was wanking his enormous cock. She then straddled the bench, and with her skirt up around her waist, she opened her legs wide, bent her knees and lowered herself onto his face. I could see the lips of her cunt were slimy and open following her frigging.

His tongue lapped around her beautiful cunt for ages until she was really panting for it. Then she shuffled along his body, and with her legs still wide apart she gave his prick a few rubs and lowered herself onto it.

She went wild as his knob slid into her and started jerking up and down on his shaft. I was wanking properly by then. There is something indescribably erotic about a lovely girl wearing high-heeled shoes, sheer seamed nylons and suspenders, getting fucked.

She was crying out and wriggling her beautiful bum wildly. Suddenly he gave a shout and heaved her high into the air as he shot his lot into her.

When they had calmed down, she climbed off him, and it was a great joy to watch her straightening the seams of her nylons and adjusting her black suspenders on her stocking-tops.

My spunk was running down the tiled wall by this time as they tidied up and returned to the club room, totally unaware of the pleasure they had provided for me. Oh, how I enjoyed myself!

Phil, London

3. FAN CLUBBING

Uniform Sighs
Mine's A Larger
Let's Meat Up Sometime
Margaret's Magic
Juicy Joanne

Jean Genie
Paper Wankies?
Very Private Medicine
More Mature

Uniform Sighs

I am a great fan of your magazine and my favourite features are Readers Wives and Striptease. What an excellent issue 17/3 was. Not only did it have these two regulars but also Request Stop featured Lesley of West Yorkshire, in a photo strip along with a letter she had written. Brilliant.

The letter was superb. I can almost feel her pussy soaking wet under her panties, her mouth soft and warm closing over my cock.

I admire her for telling us her most erotic secrets and at the same time revealing her marvellous naked charms. She has exposed herself totally to us, her body and her mind. I wonder if any of your other female readers would care to emulate Lesley's example?

Come on girls, Lesley has thrown down the gauntlet. Let's see what you can do.

B.H., W. Yorks.

Mine's A Larger

It's been some time since I bought a copy of Fiesta, but recently I saw one in the newsagents and I must say I was very pleased with it. I congratulate you on publishing the pictures of Jackie of London. There is no doubt that men are again in favour of the larger woman.

The sight of Jackie slowly disrobing to her undies and consequently those tantalising glimpses of moulds of lovely flesh which her striptease exposed left my eyes glued to the pages. Oh what joy when her gorgeous tits finally sprang into view, to be quickly followed by her lovely, meaty bum. Sheer ecstasy was the next pleasure. That lovely cunt surrounded by fatty tissue! How I would have loved to finger that large orifice, feel my fingers slipping around in the love juices.

My only regret was that Jackie was not pictured with a held-open crotch slot. I think a glimpse of that open lovehole shiny with sex juice would have made me shoot my load on the spot.

Peter, Mitcham

Let's Meat Up Sometime

I've just seen Vol 16 No 8 and have fallen in love with the blonde butcher. Everything about her is perfect — a lovely pair of tits which make your mouth water, a lovely bottom that I'd just love to give a gentle smack and a lovely pussy just right for stroking. Yes, she can have a bone off me any day of the week.

M.D., Yorks.

Margaret's Magic

I am normally a confirmed tit man, but if ever there was a sweeter, nicer-looking cunt displayed for our stimulation than Margaret of Peterhead's in Readers Wives Vol 15, No 11, then I've never had the pleasure.

Really she is quite naughty, flashing such a pussy, knowing very well it is such a lovely one that many men will admire it and wank over it. She lolls back, legs apart, her proud cunt thrust at us like a challenge, yet all the while looking much like any decent, nice lady you'd see in the supermarket. She smiles serenely out of the page, making one think, 'What is a nice girl like you doing flashing your quim?'

That's the charm of Readers Wives . . . one expects

scrubbers and gets the wholesome young mum next door.

Margaret of Peterhead fits exactly in this category. She *must* be the loveliest woman *ever* to adorn your wives feature, and obviously wholesome and respectable too. Nevertheless, flaunting her lovely naked body for all to see, she poses calm-faced, with rounded shoulders and arms, a tantalising tuft of thick dark underarm hair, smooth skin, good-sized shapely breasts and nipples and joy of joy the finest open thighs and slit of inviting cunt one could wish to see . . . or feel . . . or suck . . . or kiss . . . or fuck.

And what a hairy cunt too! The lovely luxuriant growth starts down around her rosebud anus and spreads out over her lower belly like the Nile delta. Would that I could bathe in it . . . I hereby volunteer to kiss it better or lick it clean, whatever is required, anytime of night or day. I would most dearly love to shaft it with my erect dong.

Even as I write these naughty thoughts I see Margaret's dark eyes appraising me from the printed page, as if saying: 'That cunt is special . . . not for the likes of anybody. Consider yourself fortunate I allowed you a glimpse of it.'

I've always put your letters section first. All I ask is they be reasonably believable and randifying. I resent Interchange space taken up with fillers . . . what a great mag Fiesta is etc. (we know that), or readers going on about your models' tits and bums. I skipped those letters to read how J.R. of Lancs was shagging his ma-in-law doggy-fashion, or how Student of Loughborough was having his innocent young face sat on by the great plump bare arse of his landlady. Yet here I am using up space!

All I know is I've fallen hard for a sweet dark face, a lovely mature body and the most magnificent hairy cunt anywhere. I shall keep Margaret's picture until it falls to tatters with age and use. I thank her for the privilege and do hope we'll see more of this lovely creature. Do reprint her reclining naked photo or a full frontal *close up* of her beautiful matted minge . . . and please try to cajole her to pose for a whole feature spread.

D.S., Warwicks

Juicy Joanne

I must congratulate you on publishing the pics of Joanne of Berks in Vol 15 No 7. I wish I could meet her — what a sexy body she's got. The things we could do together . . . I'll tell you the way I'd go about it — if her hubby doesn't mind.

She would be lying on the bed with just her knickers and suspenders on. I would join her and start sucking at those lovely nipples of hers, then slowly I would peel her knickers off and start to lick and kiss her, moving down her body all the time until I came to her lovely thick bush.

How I would love to kiss those lovely fanny lips of hers. I would make her come loads of times until she was lovely and wet, then I would give her the best poking she has ever had in her life. I can just imagine her legs wrapped tight around me, pumping in and out and chewing on those lovely nipples at the same time.

Whoever Joanne's husband is, he's a very lucky man indeed. God, Joanne, the things you do for me. Just looking at you makes me come my load. But just think, Joanne, when you're having a good session tonight, the only way I can think of you is by looking in Fiesta and having a lovely slow wank while adoring that lovely arse of yours.

Please print this letter, Fiesta, so that Joanne can know how much enjoyment she brings to slow wankers like me, and do try and get her in your Readers' Wives Striptease.

R.A., Lancs.

Jean Genie?

I must congratulate you on finding Jean of Cheshire for your Readers' Wives Striptease section in the Holiday Special No. 6. Jean's breasts are superb, with the nipples fully erect, and those long sensual legs encased in black stockings give her that exotic look of a high class lady of pleasure.

Please, please use your influence with her and persuade her to do more exotic poses, preferably in a tight white sweater, with her nipples fully erect, or in a white see-through blouse and of course, suspenders and stockings under a mini-dress.

I hope you can persuade her to do more work because with her earthy eroticism, I think she deserves more exposure and I expect other readers will agree with me.

Dennis, North London

Paper Wankies?

As a dedicated wanker I look forward to each edition of Fiesta with relish, and in particular the Readers' Wives section, which is unsurpassed anywhere else.

In Vol. 18 No. 1 the assembly of wives and girlfriends was simply the best I can remember. All the girls were terrific, but the one which took my breath was Ginnie of Herts.

Night after night I've slipped into bed early, and spent hours wanking to those three precious pictures of her gorgeous body. Those breasts are just wonderful. The amount of seed I've shot ought to qualify me for some sort of reward from the shareholders of Kleenex tissues. I must have upped their turnover a bit since I set eyes on Ginnie.

I've got quite a small cock, but I'd really make sure Ginnie enjoyed every inch of it if I had the chance. I can't remember any girl in a magazine giving me so much pleasure. Please bring her back for a full session — I think I'd buy up a dozen copies if you did.

Steve, Middx.

Very Private Medicine

I would like to say a big thank you to Lesley of Leeds for providing us lusty males with four superb shots of herself (Vol. 17 No. 10). I have spent many hours wanking over her gorgeous body, whilst entertaining the most delightful fantasies which go something like this.

Lesley is my private nurse and she decides one day that I need a bit of a tonic. She walks into my room as I lie in bed. She's wearing black high heels, black seamed stockings and her uniform. She walks over to my bed and pulls back the covers to reveal my rigid cock firmly grasped in my right hand.

'Naughty boy,' she says with a smile, 'Let's see what we can do about this swelling.' At which point she slowly unfastens her uniform, keeping her eyes all the time on my huge cock as I slowly begin to masturbate. As she steps out of her uniform she reveals a pair of gorgeous boobs, just ripe for suckling, and she's wearing those beautiful white knickers and suspenders.

'Now then,' she says. 'You're going to screw me like you've never screwed a woman before.' She lies on the bed next to me and I immediately get my tongue around her perfectly formed breasts, and at the same time I slip my hand inside her knickers. Her quim is wet and as I slip my fingers inside she arches her back to force her clitoris against my thumb.

We are now getting really worked up. I can hardly contain myself from coming, and I'm not even inside her yet. Lesley's hips are gyrating and she is moaning for me to give her a good tonguing.

I slip off her knickers and she opens her legs wide. I get down between her legs and start to caress her quim with my tongue. 'Harder you bastard.' She says, as she clamps my head between her stocking-clad thighs. My tongue shoots in and out, and I suck furiously at her clitoris. She comes in a shattering climax.

She lays back panting, but I've still not yet satisfied the ache in my cock. 'Come on then, let's have your prick.' I waste no time at all. I plunge into her.

'Oh you are gorgeous Lesley, I love your body.' I'm in absolute heaven as I ram myself inside her. I want it to continue but I am too turned on, I shoot gallons of spunk into her.

Unfortunately though, I'm not screwing Lesley and I end up with spunk all over my stomach. It's the next best thing though.

I just hope that you people at Fiesta can persuade Lesley to do a Readers Wives Striptease.

Dave, Coventry

More Mature

As a regular reader of Fiesta who never misses a copy, I must say that Vol 16 No 8 is one of the best yet. I always turn to Readers' Wives first in my search for the more mature, full-bodied ladies with large breasts. Then I turn to the letters section. The letter from J.W. of Crewe so echoed my own sentiments that it could almost have been written by me.

The ladies who caught my eye were Elizabeth of Devizes, Celia of the East Midlands, Diane of Portsmouth and Lin of Essex. But pride of place must go to Doreen in His 'n' Hers.

How I would love to fasten my mouth round their lovely breasts and suckle them, then bury my face between their thighs to worship at their fountains of love and quench my thirst with their love-juices.

If any of them ever wanted a devoted slave to orally satisfy them — with their hubby's permission of course — I would run post-haste to meet them. I am an older type of reader, but I still have a healthy interest in sex and I'm certainly not a 'dirty old man'. I love my wife very much, but due to an old-fashioned upbringing she thinks that sex at our age — both in our fifties — is no longer proper, even though I would still love to cunny her.

So please, let's see more full-bodied older wives in the mag to brighten the lives of us older frustrated guys who really appreciate them.

Dan, Cleveland

4. A LITTLE BIT OF SPICE

Knicker Stories
Rubbery Lady
Got A Light, Mac?
Snatch Thief
Lotta Bottle
Football Was Cancelled
Tight Spot
Sheer Fun
Feet First
Smoke Gets In Your Eyes
Drawers Full Of Memories
Alternative Blow Jobs
Silk Cut

To The Fore
Flavour Locked
Monopede Pride
Electric Tingle
Lip Service
Swinging Sporrans
DIY Dalliance
Knicker Nostalgia
Ideal Home Exhibitionist
Bather's Delight
Blitz-site Bliss
Abide A Wee

Knicker Stories

Since my early 'teens (and I'm 32 now), I've tried to beg, borrow or steal a pair of knickers from every girl, woman or lady I've fucked, fingered or been intimate with in some way. Obviously I've missed out a few times, especially in the early days when my idea of sexual intimacy as a naive schoolkid was a quick grope up the skirt of some girl behind the bicycle sheds.

But I did steal the knickers from the first girl I screwed (she was 16, I was a year older) and I suppose it was this escapade that started me off on my hobby. My rules are simple — firstly, I make a point of only asking for or stealing knickers from girls I have fucked or licked or perhaps just fingered at length; secondly, I'm not interested in freshly laundered knickers — they have to be 'used'.

I don't wear the garments myself. They are placed into separate polystyrene bags, carefully labelled with names and dates and stacked away in a special cabinet at home (I'm not married, I hasten to add, and hope to avoid being so for a few more years yet).

You'll get some idea of the scope of my love life over the past 16 years when I tell you that my knicker collection has just topped the 320 mark. They've previously adorned the bottoms and hugged the slits of all sorts of women — young, middle-aged, teenagers, a couple of matrons, short, tall, fat, skinny, black, white and a wide variety of nationalities.

Black and pink appear to be the most popular colours, with white not too far behind. The materials range from silk and plain cotton to the flimsiest of chiffon, from thick

112

elasticated material to wispy nylon, from tantalising lace to thin, clinging rubber.

And as for styles, well, I reckon I've got the lot. There's dainty, lace-trimmed little G-strings in delicate pastel colours; lots of bikini style briefs, some in nylon, others in stretch cotton; wide-legged French knickers, usually in satin with lacey frills; navy blue and white 'gym knickers'; the occasional split crutch kind in lurid reds and purples; and a reasonable selection of skin-tight panty-girdles, some with suspenders attached, others full-length corset-style.

Oddments include a pair in silver lurex, once the property of an American cheerleader; a pair of pantaloons worn by a girl in an amateur dramatic stage show; a pink panty-girdle in ultra-thin pliable rubber which once hugged the slit of a large-scale black chick; and — real treasures, these — two pairs spotted with tiny dots of blood, which bring back memories of two of the three virgins I've deflowered in my life.

Some of the knickers are heavily stained with love juices; others are only slightly discoloured. A lot depends on how quickly and profusely the lady 'wets up' and whether or not she 'comes' before removing them to fuck.

My one great regret is that the wonderous, heady aroma that a woman leaves on the gusset of her knickers when she's sexed up disappears all too quickly. The visible signs remain intact but the scent of the warm valley these knickers have 'protected' regrettably vanishes.

You could say that every pair of knickers tell a story and you'd be right. Of course, some stories are better than others — some are no more than memories. But the tale of how I got my hands on knickers No. 320 is worth telling.

I'm in business in a small way for myself and share an office with another fellow. I've never met his wife, but I've got to know her over the 'phone because she's forever ringing up trying to find out where he is (he seldom seems to go home on time and I'm pretty sure their relationship isn't all it should be).

Anyway, Heather called up one day for Brian.

'Not around,' I said. And jokingly I said: 'He's nipped out to buy you a pair of French knickers.'

'Chance would be a fine thing,' she replied. 'Anyway, I don't like French knickers.'

'So what kind do you like,' I questioned.

'I can't tell you something like that over the 'phone,' said Heather.

'Ok then, show me,' I persisted. There was a moment's silence before Heather replied: 'Don't dare me. You might get a shock.'

It was all very lighthearted and jokey, simply a bit of fun. So imagine my surprise a couple of days later when a plain white envelope arrived — with a pair of small, silky, lace-trimmed maroon knickers nestling inside. And what's more, they had most definitely been worn and still retained the delightful aroma of the wearer's sweet and syrupy slit.

But better was to follow. Around 5.30 that afternoon, Heather presented herself in the office — a slim brunette, about 34 or 35, reasonably attractive and still wearing her office clothes . . . a slim, pencil skirt and white blouse covering quite sizeable tits.

'I've come to collect my knickers,' she announced quite openly.

'Can't I keep them?' I asked.

'No, not those, they're my favourites.'

I paused. 'Ok, I'll have the ones you're wearing now in return for these,' I announced.

'You can if you want. But I don't think you'll like them,' she said. 'You see, I've been reading a dirty book all afternoon and they might be a bit . . . well, you know, a bit damp,' she said coyly.

I just couldn't believe my ears. This lady who I'd never met before was actually egging me on!

'Marvellous,' I told her. 'So, how about taking them off?'

114

Quick as a flash, she pulled her tight skirt up to her waist. 'No, that's your job. If you want them, you'll have to take them down yourself,' she replied grinning broadly.

I very nearly lost my nerve at this point. The sight was breathtaking and my eyes were riveted on Heather's legs sheathed in dark tan *stockings* held taught by a white suspender belt. And completing the picture, black nylon knickers stretched over the plump bulge between her legs.

'Well?' she said. 'Are you going to take them down?'

In milliseconds, I was on my knees in front of her, pulling her kickers down her thighs, past her knees and over her feet. The crotch of her knickers was saturated, and when I looked up, I was staggered to find that Heather had opened her legs and was blatantly exposing a big fleshy cunt with the lips already moist and inviting.

I put my hands on the insides of her thighs, but she stopped me.

'No, mustn't touch,' she chided. 'Look all you want but mustn't touch.'

I stared at her cunt until I heard her say: 'You shouldn't tease married ladies on the 'phone. Otherwise you might have to pay for it. Like this.' And as she said it, she moved slightly forward and very forcibly dragged my head between her open thighs.

No further words were necessary. Tentatively, I licked her slit until I felt the lips of her cunt opening. Then I plunged my tongue inside her, lashing the sweet inner flesh and licking every inch of her quim. I kept up my licking for maybe ten minutes before switching my undivided attention to her throbbing clit. Her thighs began to tremble and she exploded into an orgasm that must have lasted a full five minutes. Sweet, sticky come poured over my lips and into my mouth as she ground her cunt harder and harder into my face.

Finally, the trembling stopped, her breathing returned to something like normal. She stepped away, stopped to pick up her black knickers and used them to wipe her cunt dry — ensuring that I still had a good view between her legs. She then put on her other knickers and smoothed down her skirt.

'I enjoyed that,' she announced. 'It's been a long time since I had that sort of treatment.' She suddenly tossed her crumpled, sodden black knickers to me and moved to my side. Very matter of factly, she very quickly unzipped my trousers, pulled out my erect prick and wanked me furiously until my come splashed out on to the carpet.

After she'd wiped her hands on a tissue, Heather coolly announced she was late and had to dash. 'Will I see you again?' I asked.

She pondered for a few seconds. 'I haven't got that many pairs of knickers to spare, but if the answer's yes, you'll get an invitation through the post,' she replied coyly.

Now that's what I call a sexy lady. A horny bitch might be more the truth. Either way, I can assure you that opening the morning post has become one of the high points of my day!

Mark, Middx.

Rubbery Lady

While browsing through some back issues of your magazine the other night I came across a letter from Mr E.C. of Kent (Vol 17 No. 11) in which he related his experiences at the rubber-gloved hands of his wife. Now, although I have worn rubber gloves for washing up, housework etc, I had never thought of them as erotic objects, so simply out of curiosity I showed the letter to my husband. His reaction left me in no doubt as to what he thought.

Although I was a bit surprised, I've never been one to pass up an opportunity to try out some new bit of harmless kinky fun, so over the next few days I worked out an idea. The next Saturday evening my husband was watching the TV, and I went upstairs, having told him I was taking a bath. Once in our bedroom, I stripped off and then put on the items I had hidden away at the foot of the wardrobe.

The image that greeted me in the full-length mirror showed a black lacy bra, panties and suspender belt, black stockings and knee-length high-heeled black boots. However the outfit wasn't yet complete, so from a drawer I took out a new pair of pink rubber gloves and put them on. After a final look in the mirror I went downstairs, entered the lounge and walked across the room, not looking at my husband. The strangled gasp from behind me told me that whatever he had been watching on TV had suddenly ceased to hold his interest.

Turning to face him I let him have a good look, then I told him to strip. When he had done so, I said 'Go on then. You want to kiss and lick my leather boots and rubber gloves, don't you?' He did, and was down on his knees immediately. While he was kissing my boots, I allowed my gloved fingers to caress my clitoris through the silky panties I wore. The turn-on was fantastic, and I almost dragged him on top of me then and there, but that wasn't part of the plan . . .

After a little while I told him to sit on the couch, then I knelt between his legs and took his cock in my gloved hands, stroking and fondling it until he came, splattering the soft pink rubber with sticky liquid. I rubbed some of the come onto my boots and said, 'Alright, darling, now you will lick my rubber gloves clean, then you will lick my boots clean, and then you will fuck me — hard!' By the time every last drop of come was licked off, his cock was erect again and I duly received the shafting I desperately wanted.

Since then we have often used rubber gloves in our sexy sessions; sometimes I allow my husband to wear them, but only if he has earned the privilege by being my 'slave' for the day — this means a day of housework, dressed only in tights and a PVC apron. We have tried various makes of gloves, but our favourites by far are the pink or yellow medium weight gloves which are sold under the 'Marigold' trademark. They are made of beautifully soft, smooth rubber, with a textured palm surface that gives a tremendous sensation when applied to erect nipples. Initially, they also smell nice!

We would love to hear from other readers who have discovered the sexy delights of rubber gloves. How about some gloved Readers' Wives, too? I have quite a few polaroids of myself in my gloves etc. If you publish this letter I'll send some in, OK?

Susan, Fife

Got A Light Mac?

We read your magazine regularly, and Ian, my husband, has encouraged me to write this letter in the hope it may help others who are a bit worried about their partner's fetish.

In your recent article on fetishism, one of the garments mentioned was mackintoshes. Ian and I often wear mackintoshes to have sex in, although I wasn't too keen at first.

The subject came about around eighteen months ago, when Ian admitted to being turned on by women in mackintoshes. Apparently when he was younger he was seduced by a friend of his mother's. During the seduction she wore a black PVC mac and since that day he found he was turned on by women in PVC macs.

Over the next couple of months he tried to encourage me to wear a PVC mac whilst we had sex. To me a PVC mac was a cold sexless thing, but I love Ian so I decided I may as well try it out — at least once.

A local store sold a see-through PVC mac, which are so popular today. It was blue in colour and fastened with press studs. It had a draw string hood and deep slanted pockets. I bought the mac and went home.

In the privacy of our bedroom I undressed down to my underwear, and slipped the mac on. I felt a shiver as I pulled the cold blue plastic over my shoulders. My nipples became pert, and as I fastened the mac up I must admit I felt quite turned on, just in the kinkyness of it, and the contrast of my warm body against the cold plastic. Gradually the warmth of my body softened the plastic, making it supple and, yes, sexy. I imagined Ian drooling over me.

That evening after tea, I showered and put Ian's favourite perfume on, then a pair of black stockings, a high pair of stilettos, then the new acquisition. My stomach had butterflies in anticipation. As the mac went on, I fastened the studs then shouted for Ian.

He came into the bedroom and his eyes puffed out of his head. He came up to me, running his hands up my sleeves, saying how sexy I was. We kissed passionately. His tongue delved in my mouth as his hands explored my mackintosh clad body. In what seemed like a split second Ian was undressed and rubbing his body against my mac.

He went down on his knees and started to kiss my feet. Working his way up, he licked and kissed my mac. I found this a great turn-on and my vagina was hungry for Ian's cock.

Once again he was down on his knees. This time he unfastened the lower part of the mac and his tongue delved into me. I couldn't hold myself and came in a wonderful orgasm, but Ian wasn't finished. He stood up and lifted the supple mac to reveal my bum. His huge cock went up me and I caught sight of ourselves in the mirror. My mac was twisting and creasing around me. I knew from that moment I would never think of mackintoshes for just keeping out of the rain.

Ian withdrew and pushed me onto the bed. Pulling open the mac, he plunged into me and we came together. What a climax!

I have been hooked since then, and I have acquired four more macs of different styles and colours. Occasionally I dress Ian in a pair of stockings with one of my see through macs on. It's a lovely sensation feeling the smooth plastic rubbing against my breasts. Even if I see another woman in a raincoat, I wonder if she wears it to have sex in. If she doesn't, she's missed a lot of pleasure — so come on ladies don't just wear your mac for the wet, wear it for sex.

I'm sure it must be more common than we realise. How about some Readers' Wives and Husbands in their mackintoshes or in the Request Stop? You mention women in wellies — well wellies and mackintoshes go together.

For Christmas this year, Ian is buying me a black rubber mackintosh. I can hardly wait. Perhaps if your readers are interested I will write to you then. I hope this letter spurs on more fetishism.

Beverley, Glasgow

Snatch Thief

Quite often letters have mentioned a fetish shared by many males, namely knicker snatching. However, I have never heard of the fetish among females mentioned.

Ever since my school days I've been stealing other girls knickers, and cannot get out of the habit. I think I first did it out of spite, and can remember asking to be excused during P.E. in order to carry out the theft. I would hide the pair of knickers where they would not be found, and during the afternoon I would leave a note in class letting the boys know a certain girl was knickerless; thus getting my revenge.

I can remember 'borrowing' underwear when I left home and shared a large house with several other girls of my age. After removing the dirty knickers from a particular girl's room, I would inspect them, sniff them and sometimes wear them before hiding them in my case.

Whenever one of the girls returned from a date where a fuck would have taken place, I wouldn't rest until I got my cunt into the spunk-stained crotch of the girl's panties.

If anyone else has this fetish, please write in as I would like to hear more about it.

Linda, W. London

Lotta Bottle

T.T. of Berks asks in Vol. 16 No. 9 whether he should give up the baby's dummy. My advice to him is no — why not expand this delight? Let me explain. When my wife first had our baby she breast fed her for about six months. She used to let me suck any spare milk from her breast and this gave us both a lot of pleasure.

When her milk ran out, after about a year — I continued at the breast longer than the baby — I greatly missed the joy of sucking milk from a tit. One day as I was getting ready for bed my wife said she had a surprise for me, and she produced a baby's bottle full of milk. But there was one condition. She said if I wanted to act like a baby then I must dress as one.

She had also bought a large white towel to use as a nappy, plus pins, a pair of plastic pants (you can buy adult sizes from chain chemists) and a dummy.

She made me dress in one of her baby doll nighties, and then she put the nappy and plastic pants on me. We lay on the bed with my head resting on her breast, and she fed me as a mother feeds her baby.

As soon as I started to suck the milk from that teat I felt as randy as hell, and when I had finished my bottle she checked to see if I had wet my nappy. After that we made love in a way we hadn't done for years.

Before this happened to me, if anyone had said that they got pleasure from dressing and acting like a baby I would have thought that they must be kinky. But I will never forget the pleasure and joy of our first baby fuck. We now use our baby game as a regular part of lovemaking — not every time, but about once or twice a month.

Tom, Bucks

Football Was Cancelled

My wife goes to evening classes and has made friends with Jean, an attractive woman in her 30s. My wife had borrowed a book from Jean and I offered to drop it round. It was a cold, wintry Saturday afternoon and Jean's husband, as usual, had gone to watch football.

We were in the kitchen and I noticed a pair of blue, cotton D.K.s on the clothes-horse. Pointing to them, I asked if she was washing for her mother. She laughed and said they were hers, and although not very glamorous, they were lovely and warm in the cold weather.

I said that Directoire knickers may not be glamorous but they were sexy in a basic, earthy way. With that, she hoisted her skirt up to her waist to reveal white cotton Directoire knickers and thick black stockings.

'What do you think of these?' she asked.

'That really turns me on,' I exclaimed.

'I don't believe you.'

Quickly unzipping my jeans, I pushed them down to my knees. She gasped at the sight of my erect, rock-hard penis. She said that it would be a pity to waste that, lowered her knickers to her knees and lay back on the kitchen table. Her white suspender belt with wide suspender-straps and black stocking-tops framed her hairy cunt.

'Fuck me, fuck me,' she pleaded, raising her knees to her chest.

I pistoned in her 19-to-the-dozen, finally pumping my spunk into her. When we had finished she nipped up to the bathroom, leaving me in the kitchen. She returned to find me with the blue knickers in my hands.

'Kinky!' she said. 'You'll be wearing them next.'

For a laugh, I took off my shoes and jeans and put on the blue knickers. I was standing there in sweater, knickers and socks when Dave, her husband, walked in. The football match had been cancelled.

We stood like statues until suddenly Dave started to shake with laughter. He pointed at me, fell into a chair and roared with laughter. Relieved, Jean and I laughed too and she explained how I had come to put the knickers on . . . and it all ended happily. I still see Jean on Saturday afternoons . . . making sure the football isn't cancelled.

When I'm with Jean, the atmosphere is electric . . . she lights up . . . I'm switched on . . . her cunt's ever-ready . . . and I can't wait to get plugged!

Joe, Bucks

Tight Spot

In response to L.T. of Beds . . . yes, love, I for one did appreciate the picture of you in tights, and I'm sure I'm not in a minority.

After holding a mini-survey amongst my girlfriends it seems that we are all bum-watchers. In fact, all my friends are in agreement that the build of a male ballet dancer gets 10½ out of 10 in the turn-on stakes. Those gorgeous meaty buttocks and muscular legs make my quim wet with excitement. My husband can't understand why a semi-ignoramus like me tunes in with such eagerness to ballet programmes on TV.

What I'd ideally love to see is a picture of a man, smooth skinned, not hairy, wearing a pair of very sheer seamed tights, naturally a back-view, with the sole of one foot exposed. I happen to believe that the pad of the male big toe is one of the most erotic objects imaginable.

It's pointless asking my hubby to pose like this as he's a bit of a spindly weed, to put it mildly.

So are there any meaty males among your readers man enough and unconventional enough to take up my challenge?

Ruth, Glos.

Sheer Fun

Reading Fiesta Vol 16 No 2 my eyes were soon drawn to the pic on page 79 of L.T. of Beds showing off his gorgeous cock for all us lucky girl readers to see. I love men in black tights, the mere sight of this is enough to make my pussy ooze with anticipation.

It reminds me of a boy I met called Kevin. He was a biker and used to ride around on a CZ400. He was a friend of one of my ex-boyfriends and used to call round to our house which we shared with other students.

One day he arrived there soaking wet. The rain had soaked right through his leathers and jeans. I told him he might find some dry clothes in the bathroom.

I don't mind admitting that I fancied him like mad, and when he returned from the bathroom wearing nothing but my black nylon tights I felt as though I just couldn't live any longer without his prick. The tights emphasised the wonderful masculine contours of his legs and his prick stood out like a clothes prop inside them.

Inevitably we ended up in bed. Kevin cut a slit in the tights to unleash his massive meat dagger with its gorgeous purple head, and he kept them on while we fucked all afternoon. I couldn't keep count of the number of orgasms I had, it must have been eight or nine.

That was a one-off occasion and I've never had the pleasure of an encore, though I still fantasise about meeting a well-hung boy who likes wearing black tights.

Bertha, Lancs.

Feet First

Everyone seems to worship a favourite part of the female body. Some like bottoms, others cunts, and a lot seem to go for tits. Personally I like hairless cunts, but above all else I go wild over bare feet. For years I have enjoyed looking at girls' feet, in trains, swimming baths, on the beach, and just recently in a mixed sauna.

They vary so much. I prefer the toenails to be painted, but any well-formed female foot can give me an erection without any problems, and even staring at a bare foot for a short while can cause me to ejaculate. I often masturbate in my bedrom while looking at girls' feet in magazines.

Of course it has been no trouble to get girls to allow me to kiss and suck their feet. To gently suck a few toes gives pleasure to both parties. One of my girlfriends who is a student nurse loves to lie stark naked on a low armchair while I slowly suck her toes and lick her feet all over. She masturbates while I do this and usually climaxes several times. She also plays with her breasts which are nice and firm and don't need a bra.

But another girl whose toes fascinate me and who lets me suck them also gets a stong urge to piddle. Twice in fact she has been wriggling about on my sofa and despite a brave attempt to hold herself she has failed to warn me on time and ended up peeing all over the covers.

This has fascinated me because she has an utterly smooth shaven cunt and to be sucking her toes and watching her urine simply pouring out made me start tossing myself and shooting spunk all over the carpet. Quite a messy session all in all, but great fun.

I'm sure urolagnia is far more widespread than people imagine. After all, peeing is quite natural and essential and I can't see anything dreadful in two people of the opposite sex wanting to do it openly during a sex session. Two years ago at a swimming baths, I spied through a small hole in the cubicle wall and saw a young woman doing a pee while standing up, legs wide apart on the sloping floor. She certainly seemed in need of it and the expression on her face was one of joyous relief and pleasure.

Finally, I'd just like to say that I've been tossed off by girls using their toes, but the only thing is, I always come too quickly. It's all over in a couple of minutes, and then the girls usually dip their toes into the warm spunk that lies on my stomach.

Martin, Middx.

Smoke Gets In Your Eyes

I get really turned on by attractive women smoking. I travel to work every day by tube and always sit in the smoking compartment. I often come in my trousers as I watch some gorgeous thing drawing on a king-size cigarette as though it were a slender smouldering cock between her lips. Even a plain girl can be erotic to me if she has a cigarette between her fingers, providing she's not dressed like a tramp.

Neither my wife, Lorna, nor myself are heavy smokers but we have a large collection of Polaroid pics in which she is holding a cigarette between her long red-nailed fingers or drawing on one between her lips, either naked or dressed in some erotic gear which shows off her gorgeous cunt and nipples.

One of my favourite pics is of her dressed in a patent leather cupless bra with matching suspenders, thigh-length boots and gloves that reach the top of her arms but leave the fingers exposed. On this she is sitting on my face with my tongue buried in her cunt whilst she holds her head slightly back, eyes half closed with pleasure, and draws on an extra long Dunhill. The things you can do with a Polaroid and a remote control device!

In fact, nearly every photo I have of Lorna in a sexual position shows her smoking, except for the ones where we are actually shagging, although there are some pictures of her on my lap with my cock inside her cunt, where she is either smoking or holding a cigarette while I play with her 38" tits.

Another favourite pic is one of her taken in an armchair after I had shagged her. This is really erotic as she is wearing black suspenders, fish-net stockings, black shoes and those long gloves. Her legs are wide apart and her hole is leaking spunk onto her stockings as she smokes a cigarette, a picture of such eroticism that only a woman who has just orgasmed, her nipples fully erect, can portray.

I'm toying with the idea of taking one with my cock in her mouth and a cigarette hanging from her cunt, and if she agrees I'll do just that.

Do other readers share my fetish? I hope they'll write in and maybe send their Polaroids too, I don't think I'd stop coming . . .

Tom, London

Drawers Full Of Memories

Fiesta Vol 15 No 9 was great stuff. How about that Mary from Hampshire? Sexy, with class. The way she handled those French knickers! And I loved the Big Girls feature, as it reminded me of my own experience with a plump nurse called Nancy a few years ago.

Nancy had terrific knockers, a fine 40C, and she was justly proud of them. She loved to play with them as she sat astride me and then bend over to stuff them into my mouth. To my delight, she also shared my enthusiasm for knickers and she once sent me a pair through the post after she'd worn them all night — pale blue panties with white lace. I carried them in my breast pocket all day so that I could inhale the lovely aroma of cunt, and at night I wore them in bed.

We shared French knickers also, but my greatest thrill was when she agreed to wear pink Directoires with me. Nancy loved to be sucked off, and I first gave her a good licking through the gorgeous silky pink nylon.

Then she demanded it on her bare flesh, so I decided to suck her off inside them. I lay on the bed, she got on her hands and knees on top of me, her head towards my feet. Then I put my head inside the lovely rippling voluminous pink drawers and set to work with my tongue on her warm wet cunt with its big protruding lips.

I love cunts like that, they make a marvellous mouthful. Being inside the Directoires concentrated all the delicious flavour and smell of her femininity and I licked her greedily, drinking the sexy secretions of her dripping pussy.

P.F., Yorks.

Alternative Blow Jobs

Having been an avid reader of Fiesta for a number of years, I have had lots of pleasure reading your letters when on the oil rigs. I would like to tell the readers of an experience that happened to me a number of years ago that set me off on my fetish.

After completing a trip on an oil rig, my first stop was a local bar, where I had a few drinks and got talking to a beautiful redhead. I bought her a few drinks, one thing led to another and we went back to her flat.

As I was making love to her, I broke wind. I was terribly embarrassed and extremely apologetic. At this she started to giggle and said it didn't matter. She then insisted on pulling the sheet over her head and breathing deeply. I started laughing at this, and she explained that the smell of men's farts turned her on.

Later she explained that she also enjoyed it for her partner to smell the aroma of her farts. So that evening I took her out for a drink. She insisted I bought her half pints of stout. She also had cheese and onion sandwiches. This was guaranteed to give her flatulence. We returned to her flat and went straight to the bedroom to make love.

When we got in bed together, we engaged in a heavy petting session. She then pushed me down on her to perform cunnilingus. I realised what might happen and wasn't at all sure what my reaction would be. But at this point I was past caring.

I licked and sucked her juicy, red-haired pussy. I was licking it for at least 10 minutes and it completely went out of my head what she intended to do. She started to orgasm. As she reached her peak, there was a sudden explosion between her buttocks, and a warm waft of wind blew down my chest. I inhaled deeply and the smell of her love juice mixed with the heady aroma of her expulsion made me feel euphoric. I was totally surprised at the way this affected me, and even further surprised to discover that I had ejaculated a vast amount of spunk.

For several months after this we met regularly and

played similar games. We deliberately ate foods, such as beans, cheese, pickled eggs and spicy Indian take-away, so that all our love making would always come to a satisfactory aromatic conclusion.

Alas she had to move away, and I have found difficulty finding a partner who shares this fetish. I still eat the same foods and fart regularly during solo masturbation, and think of the times we had together.

The one drawback to my fetish, is that I tend to break wind at all times of the day. This is somewhat unpleasant for the rig crew who have to share my cabin.

I would very much like to find another lady friend who is interested in this subject. I would also like to hear from any readers who have had similar experiences to relate.

Alex, North Sea

Silk Cut

I have just found a new cure for smoking that can't fail. I pass it on, as I am sure it will work with your readers. It all started in a pub when my girlfriend and I agreed we smoked too much. She bet me I couldn't give it up for a week, and as a stake bet me my beard. I agreed, but added 'you can shave my beard off if I fail, but if you fail I can shave off your "whiskers",' She giggled and, at first, said no. But before the evening was out she said she wanted to quit smoking, and that was quite an incentive!

Well, I made it through the first day and the second, and then on the third I happened to mention to one of the girls in the office that Janet and I were giving up smoking for a bet. (I didn't mention the stakes, of course.)

'Oh! What did you win,' she replied, 'Janet is still smoking!'

Sure enough, I went along to Janet's office (we work for the same firm) and not only was she smoking — the ashtray was loaded. She saw me looking into the office and nearly choked on her cigarette. I poked my head round the corner of the office and whispered, 'See you tonight. We'll go to my place.'

'Can we make it tomorrow night please,' she replied, 'I haven't much on then.' That's a code we use. When she says she's got a lot on it means she is wearing tights and panties and her normal bra. When she says 'I haven't much on,' she means she has only got a skimpy half-bra, suspender-belt and stockings.

Well, she obviously wanted to pay her bet in style, who could refuse? In fact it gave me a bit of a thrill to think she'd have to spend all the next day with just a half-bra, belt and stockings under her dress. I wondered what the boss or the other girls would have thought if they'd known.

Next lunch time I took her to the local and we had lunch in the corner, where I took the opportunity to feel her stocking tops, and I could just feel her 'whiskers'. I had to stop as her nipples began to swell, and in a half-bra everyone would have seen them pushing her dress out.

She said she was sure her boss had noticed the suspender line when she did some filing in his office. Several times he had asked her to do silly jobs that caused her to bend over. She giggled. 'If he's like that over suspenders, I wonder what he'd be like if he knew I hadn't any knickers on, or that my 'whiskers' were going down the plug this evening?'

Do you know, she was looking forward to it! She told me later she had dreaded it at first but the outfit, and the effect it had on her boss (and me) had made her feel quite randy, and she thought to herself 'Well they're only hairs, and I don't need them anyway — but what a nice way to lose them!'

Straight from work I took her out for a few drinks and a meal. I was really enjoying taking her round knowing that she was bare underneath. Although we'd very often done it, this was different. Tonight she wasn't bare for the usual reasons — tonight was special.

We wound up at my place eventually, and after a few

drinks and a lot of petting I said, 'It's time to collect on my bet.'

I took off her dress and nearly changed my mind. She was so great it was all I could do to keep my mind on the business in hand. Anyway, she lay back on the sofa on a towel I produced (just as well I had the previous night to prepare everything), and stretched her legs wide apart.

I had the scissors to hand, and I snipped off all the long hairs. Then, with a bowl of hot water, a razor, soap and brush, I lathered her. She looked down at her pussy and said 'Goodbye whiskers.' And goodbye it was. I went all over her pussy, right up between her legs, and when I wiped her with a cloth she was bare — just the odd hair I'd missed. I changed blades, lathered her again and went all over it once more. This time when I wiped her and washed her there wasn't a whisker to be seen.

It was fabulous. I kissed and licked her until she was moaning with joy. Then I sprinkled her with talc and carried her to the bedroom. We had a fantastic night. She kept feeling herself and crooning how smooth she felt. I could hardly get enough. Even when we woke in the morning we had another session, until I suddenly remembered we had to go to work.

She didn't have time to go home and get changed, and so she would have to go to work in the same clothes she had worn the day before. When we came out of my flat it suddenly struck her. Wow! 'I feel cold she whispered.' Now she hadn't even hairs to cover her, and it made quite a difference. (I wouldn't know, but she assured me it did!)

Anyway, we just about made it to the office in time. Janet told me it was the longest day in the office she had ever known. She swears the other girls guessed there was something special that was different, and her boss not only kept getting her into his office, he offered her a job as his secretary, with a nice rise.

Janet swears he guessed, especially when she bent over his desk and he saw down the front of her dress. It was at that point that he offered her the job.

131

Would you believe Janet was sure I would weaken, and so we renewed the bet! Only this time she insisted I didn't collect until Saturday. In fact it has become our regular Saturday thing. Sometimes hardly any hair has grown at all. But she still lays, legs apart, while I lather her and shave her again 'because she has been naughty and smoked'. I'd gladly buy her a packet any time!

I love it, especially the licking and kissing. But mostly the session afterwards — she admits for her it's a great turn on too. Last thought. All this started because she didn't like my beard. So I shaved it off. A bit pointless her being smooth and my whiskers getting in the way, wasn't it? I still don't smoke, and Janet is down to one a week — Friday evening!

Dave, Shrops

To The Fore

I am always amazed to read so many letters from your male readers on the subject of their penises and the attitude of their partners towards their precious equipment. It clearly demonstrates the selfishness of many men who seem to believe that the sun rises and sets on the end of a penis.

So many men seem to complain when a girl insists on forcing back a tight foreskin. But I think they are missing the point when they forget that it is the girl who is on the receiving end of this organ. She is looking at it, handling it, accepting it inside her body, sometimes sucking it, so it is not surprising that she feels a need to see exactly what it is she is about to receive.

Two of my three boyfriends possessed long tight foreskins and I consider that I was quite justified in stretching them back, though I am aware that this can cause some discomfort. But there is no way of knowing if the guy is healthy when his knob is tightly sheathed, he could transmit thrush or something far worse. Most men make no attempt to remove smegma from the folds inside their foreskin, and in fact this can be difficult if the opening is very small.

For many men it will take some time and patience to open up the foreskin before it will roll right back. Those who cannot be bothered to attend to this should not be surprised if their wives or girlfriends insist on peeling the skin right back before they oblige with any form of love-play. I would certainly recommend every girl to pull the skin back far enough to see the inside surface of the foreskin. If this causes too much pain the first time she will have to persevere and gradually pull back a little more every time.

Most men seem to be obsessed with oral sex and expect their partner to open her mouth as well as her legs, so she is surely entitled to examine a knob before she takes it into her mouth or teases it with her tongue.

I have found the average well-groomed body and the cutest prick can look great and smell nice — until the moment that the foreskin is pulled back.

My experience does not extend to any encounter with a circumcised male, but the variations of shape and colour I have seen are quite fascinating. My favourite type, just for the record, is long and tapering without any prominent veins. A knob which is bluish-mauve when flaccid and deep beetroot when erect is a definite turn-on.

Maureen, Devon

Flavour Locked
I was fascinated to read about the infibulation of the penis. One of your readers doubted whether or not it can be achieved. I can assure her that it certainly can — providing the man has an average length of foreskin.

My husband has to travel a lot in his work and is sometimes away for up to three or four nights. The temptations, I suspect, can be hard to overcome, and I insisted finally that his foreskin was pierced and a tiny jewelled padlock inserted to keep the opening reduced to a minimum.

At first he told me it was uncomfortable when he got an erection, but I'm happy to say that within six months his foreskin has stretched sufficiently to allow a good strong erection while the ring is still in place.

When he first wore the device the intention was that it would be removed on the nights when he was not staying away from home. However, I enjoy seeing his prick adorned and his knob constricted by the foreskin. I now like him to leave it on all the time — except of course when we are making love. He has always been very juicy under the foreskin, but you can imagine the amount of natural lubrication and spunk built up when I unlock his foreskin and peel it back behind the knob.

I'm delighted by the results and I notice that my husband is in a state of near permanent erection whenever he is with me, especially now that he has to behave himself when he's not with me. I'm not sure if he is able to wank himself while wearing my little ornament, but he claims that it is impossible and I'm inclined to believe him.

It would be a brave man to chat up a girl while wearing such a device, and any wife would be happy with the knowledge that her husband was saving all his spunk just for her.

My husband enjoys sucking pussy and when he pushes the hood back and licks my clitoris I have a marvellous close-up view of his swollen knob under his stretched foreskin before I finally give him his freedom.

It's a great deal of fun, we both enjoy it and I suggest other ladies try it on their husbands and write to tell you of their own experiences.

Sarah, London

Monopede Pride

I agree with D.B. of Coventry — we one-legged women should make the most of ourselves and not try to hide or be ashamed of our bodies. I have been a monopede for my entire 37 years, having been born with a deformed right leg which was amputated in infancy, so I really have known nothing else.

From my earliest years I realised that having one leg made me an object of interest, and I loved it. Obviously this was before I found out that there could be any sexual connotation. This I discovered in my teens while staying with my aunt and uncle. At that age I had cropped hair, broad shoulders and narrow hips like a boy, and when dressed in jeans and a shirt, few strangers would ever have took me for a girl. I always wore trunks instead of a swimsuit.

One day I was by the pool at my auntie and uncle's house when I heard a car pull up. I thought nothing of it at first, then into the garden came my 19-year-old cousin. I hadn't seen him for a couple of years, and now the gangly teenager I remembered had become the most fabulous muscular man. He was wearing just sandals and shorts, sporting a super tan, and all I could do was exclaim, 'Wow!'

I was so taken up with the effect he was having on me that I quite forgot the effect that finding his one-legged cousin half-naked in the garden must have been having on him. Standing up, I chirped, 'Don't I get a kiss then?' He was trembling as he put his hands on my shoulders and kissed me.

'It's just like kissing a boy,' he remarked.

I wasn't quite sure how to take this, but I was beginning to feel the size of the difference between us, and it was obvious that his shorts were inadequate at concealing the bulging equipment inside them. I thought I had better say something to relieve the tension and said, 'I only look like a boy with my trunks on . . .' I soon discovered after that remark that my cousin was turned on by my body with its uninterrupted Y-shape.

To show my body off to the best advantage I walk with the aid of a single crutch and have done for twenty five years. That's how I met my husband. Over the years I had many lovers who were fascinated by my monopede body. But at twenty I came face to face with such a vison of wonder that it was love at first sight.

It was in a Brighton pub one summer. I was wearing a cotton dress, which is a rare thing for me, when in walked a guy in his late twenties. He was tall with a mass of black curly hair and he was so hirsute that he looked like an animal. He carried his shirt carelessly in one hand, and as soon as he walked in I could see that he was wearing a peg-leg, the rubber-tipped base being quite visible under the bottom of his jeans.

This keen swimmer, sailor and body-builder had lost his leg just above the knee in a road accident when he was 27, and he had decided from the outset not to try pretending that all was just as before. However good an artificial leg is, it never looks realistic.

Anyway, we chatted, then went back to his place and fucked in the hall because we couldn't even wait to get upstairs. That first sex with my Adonis was with him wearing his wooden leg, and now I always make him wear it when we fuck, even in bed. I love that thick straight shaft of wood which serves him as a leg.

Even now, at 46, there is not a scrap of fat on him, he is as strong and muscular as when I first saw him, with his extreme hairiness and an endowment that would do justice to a horse. In my opinion an 11″ prick is just right for a 16-stone superstud.

Tina, London

Electric Tingle

With every new issue of Fiesta my husband immediately turns to Readers' Wives to see how many, if any, have shaven cunts like myself. If one of them has, then it's a real turn-on for us both. We always wonder who does the shaving, he or she. Does it lead to a fuck if he does it, or does she get herself worked up into masturbating if she does it herself?

You may wonder why we are both so interested in the subject. Well it all started three years ago when, after hundreds of fucks, I had not become pregnant. I went to see my doctor and finally ended up in hospital having one of these small corrective operations. I used to have a very hairy pussy, but in preparation for the operation all this was removed, leaving me with a bald cunt.

No sooner did I get home than Trevor wanted to see what I looked like shaven. It gave him the biggest and hardest horn I have ever known him to have and I certainly got well and truly fucked.

But that wasn't the end of the story. As the hairs began to grow again it got all prickly down there and felt most uncomfortable when my panties rubbed against it. I mentioned this to Trevor and he suggested I kept it shaved and even suggested doing it for me there and then. I was all for it, knowing that it would probably end up with us fucking. But little did I know just what was in store.

Trevor only has an electric shaver and always uses it in the bathroom. So there I was, dressed just in my bra and blouse, sitting on the edge of the kitchen table while Trevor got to work with the shaver.

What need has a girl for a vibrator with one of these at hand? It's a wonder I wasn't electrocuted as I got so wet as Trevor smoothed me off. Then he held the shaver over my clit area and that clinched it. I came, and hardly had I got my breath back before Trevor had his prick out and was shagging me hard and fast across the kitchen table.

I have been bald ever since. Sometimes Trevor shaves me, and sometimes I do it myself while he watches. I always come. I never thought I would be able to masturbate with Trevor watching, but to do it while shaving my cunt seems different somehow. We always end up having a good fuck — and I'm still not pregnant!

C.C., Middx.

Lip Service

I moved to the Midlands a few years ago, where I met a woman who worked in a bookshop. She was separated from her husband, but although her role as mother and provider was full-time, we still managed to find time for some fun.

She was good in bed, and would bite my penis when I asked her to. One day I asked her to bite hard — and she did! I wanted to tell her to stop, but didn't. I found that the longer I tolerated it, the more sexual gratification it gave, and the thought of her teeth marks on my flesh satisfied my carnal desires.

We split up after a while, but we're still good friends.

My present lady is married, but her husband is not much good in bed. While he is on night shifts, I visit her house and we enjoy each other's company in bed.

It's a purely sexual relationship, and it always leaves me satisfied, as it does my lady friend. Her fellatio is great and she more than satisfies my desires.

I've always been fascinated by women's mouths and their application of lipstick. One day I asked her to apply some of her lipstick to my penis. She was cautious at first, but I obliged. Now she often asks me if I want her to paint my member.

She has even caressed it with mascara and eye-shadow. That sends me into the realms of happiness, especially when she uses her tongue to lick it off. Funny though, when I attempt cunnilingus, she pushes me away and says it's dirty.

John, Bucks

Swinging Sporrans

I read with great interest the letter from N.C., Scotland in Vol 15 No 1 about his 'kilt fetish'. I've always found girls, even quite mature ladies in kilts a real turn-on, though I can't say my interest ever amounted to a fetish. But one of my early sexual experiences was with a girl wearing a kilt.

This happened in about 1971, when I was nineteen. My girlfriend came into my bedroom one day to ask me to come out for a walk with her. But seeing this delightful 18-year-old before me, with her shoulder-length brown hair, floral blouse filled out by pert breasts, suede knee-boots, and the shortest skirt I'd ever seen her wearing — a mini-kilt which exposed more than half the length of her thighs — I decided the walk would have to wait. We never went as far as intercourse, though we often stimulated each other to orgasm in other ways.

I drew her into my arms and kissed her passionately. Next thing I knew, we were both lying on the floor and I was urgently pressing the hardness inside my trousers against her abdomen.

She opened my trousers at the waist, and unzipped them, then reached into my underwear. She ran her nails down my belly, scratching my pubic hair and 'accidentally' brushing the tip of my twitching cock. My balls contracted with the unbearable anticipation, then her hand curled coolly around my hot member.

Her thumb and forefinger were circled around the base of my cock so that the palm of her hand enveloped the rest of it, the glans pointing towards her wrist. She began to stroke me in a loose grip that she knew drove me crazy.

I slipped my knee between her legs and moved it towards her crotch. She herself grew excited, and the on-off pressure of her thighs on mine, was unbearably stimulating.

Because of her basic shyness she was afraid to look at my cock, so she would close her eyes whenever she masturbated me. This gave me a chance to ogle her legs. They looked great encased in tan-coloured tights, and I began to run my hand up and down her firm thighs, loving the feel of the nylon over her firm flesh.

As she stroked faster, she began to breathe erratically, and I edged her mini-kilt up her legs until I could see her blue nylon panties. I rubbed the edge of my hand back and forth between her legs, her juices soaking through her panties and on to my finger. I tried to imagine what the friction of nylon against her clitoris must feel like, and that only increased my excitement.

I couldn't take my eyes off her legs, off the way she dug her boot-heel into the carpet as she squeezed down on my thigh. The insistent stroking became too much, the churning in my guts, in my balls reached its peak, and we both moaned as I came (I think she must have climaxed too), me gripping the flesh of her nylon-clad thigh as the spunk arched out of my cock, soaking the sleeve of her blouse.

In bed that night I just had to jerk myself off thinking of her in that mini-kilt and those high-heeled boots. It's an experience I'll never forget.

J.T., Glasgow

DIY Dalliance

I've been happily married to John for six years now. We live in a nice semi in Croydon and our sex life is reasonable. But, for some time I've had my eyes on the young man living next door. I'd often caught him giving me admiring glances and although adultery was the last thing on my mind, I often wondered what it would be like. *(A contradiction here? — Ed.)*

Anyway, my husband had gone away for a week on a training course and as a surprise for him I decided to decorate the spare bedroom while he was away. I took all the junk out and, with a bit of help from a DIY manual, I took up the carpet and removed the doorhandle in order to do a really professional job.

140

On the Thursday I had the windows open and was painting the outside of the window frame when there was a bang. The door had been blown shut by a gust of wind. I thought nothing of it until I decided to take a break for a cup of tea and a visit to the loo, which I had neglected for some time as I was so engrossed in the job. To my horror, I had left the door handles outside the room, on the landing, and I couldn't open the door.

I tried everything, but all in vain. By now the call of nature was desperately urgent as I was unable to come up with a solution to my pressing problem. I couldn't pee on the floor, and there were no pots or tins anywhere in the bare room to relieve at least some of the pressure. I leaned out of the window and hoped someone would pass by who could rescue me. There, coming down the road, was Alan, the neighbour. I waved to him and he came up the garden path. I told him to go round to the back door, come in the house and release me. I didn't tell him of my other predicament because I was embarrassed, but when I heard him on the stairs I told him to hurry up.

He asked me why and I told him that I was desperate for the loo and that I'd wet myself if he didn't hurry. I had my hands between my legs as he fiddled about on the other side of the door, and I asked him what was taking so long. He replied that he got really turned on by girls who wet their pants. I thought about this statement for a while and I realised that by rubbing my crotch to hold my pee, I was turning myself on as well!

As the door opened I ran out to the loo, but I couldn't get the straps and buttons of my dungarees undone in time, and I just sat on the loo and let loose my pent up pee. The door was open and Alan just stared at my crotch as the material darkened, and the pee poured through.

When I had finished, I could see the manly bulge in Alan's trousers and I was strangely turned on. I hadn't wet myself like this since I was a teenager and the wet fabric felt good against my crotch. He came over to me and casually undid the straps and buttons I couldn't undo before. The soaking dungarees fell to the floor leaving me in my wet knickers and tee shirt. He kissed me and then rubbed my clit through my soaking pants. I undid his trousers and stroked his rock hard prick. Then he lowered me to the floor and, pulling my pants to one side, quickly slid his tool up my now soaking cunt.

The screw didn't last long and we both came noisily and satisfyingly. He dressed and said if ever I was in need again, I should go and see him. I didn't tell my husband anything when he got back, but he was pleased with the room! I sometimes see Alan, but we have never yet had the opportunity to repeat the experience.

Tina, Croydon

Knicker Nostalgia

Congratulations on your lovely Directoire display. I well remember how, thirty or more years ago, they were still in fairly common use, even among young ladies, such as I was myself at the time. Even the schoolgirls in those days wore knickers that were like mini-bloomers, very different from the briefly cut ones of today. Instead of being virtually legless, they had elasticated legs extending a few inches down the thighs. In winter they were of snug cotton interlock, and in summer of light and silky celanese.

One comment from a reader who pleaded for an article or picture that combined his interest in bloomers and in girls peeing was of special significance to me, because during my schooldays, and for some years afterwards, I used to love to wet my knickers and got a regular thrill from the feeling of daring to be so naughty. There was something especially sexy about peeing in those lovely bloomers which stayed wet for ages afterwards, especially the cotton or fleecy lined ones.

On the other hand, the thrill of wetting in the celanese ones was just as great, even though the feeling was different. When I wanted to be especially naughty I used to bend over on purpose and display an inch or two of wet knickers for a moment.

I sometimes feel sorry that most young girls these days will never have the pleasure of wearing — and wetting — these lovely bloomers — unless of course they go in for the lace-edged bloomers which seem largely to have replaced Directoires for winter-time wear. Perhaps some of them do still wear the genuine thing and find them both comfortable and sexy.

Claire, Yorks.

Ideal Home Exhibitionist

I've been reading your magazine since I found my younger brother's collection hidden in a cupboard while he was away on holiday. He and his wife had gone away and left me to look after their house, and while tidying up I stumbled across the last four years' copies of Fiesta, and started to read them. Most of the letters were just the normal exaggerated fantasies ('I've got a 10-inch willy and this is how I screwed 8 girls in 2 hours . . .') but I was interested to find a number of letters on the subject of knicker-wetting. I've been fascinated by this branch of sex since an incident I'll describe later, but I thought I was some kind of a freak. Now I'm reassured to see there are plenty of other girls who do it.

The incident happened when I was at college. We had been out drinking, and we got invited to a party out of town. In the general chaos I forgot to relieve myself, and as soon as I got comfy I became aware that I badly needed a pee. I asked the driver to find the nearest ladies loo, but when we found one it was closed. I decided I'd have to hang on until we got there, but I soon realised I wasn't going to make it, and when we were half-way there I told the driver to stop or he'd have a wet back seat.

He stopped quickly, but in a very inconvenient place, as there was no cover to hide myself. So I waddled along to

143

the nearest tree, with both hands holding my crotch. When I got there I could feel the flood gates weakening, and as I hoisted up my skirt I could feel the pee start to leak out. I desperately tried to get my pants off, but when I let go of my skirt it dropped down into the line of fire. By now I could feel the pee running down my leg so I just held up my skirt and let the pee pour through my panties. Afterwards I stood there shaking.

I thought about taking the panties off, but that would have meant throwing them away, as I could hardly take them back to the car, so I just readjusted them a bit and went back to the car and sat down. I asked if anyone had seen anything, and the answer was fortunately no.

When we got to the party one of the other people in the car came up to me and said he could see I'd wet myself. I was stunned at first, but he pointed to my bum, and I realised that my wet pants had soaked my skirt when I sat down. I went bright red and nodded. He said not to worry, he'd walk behind me.

The party was in full swing, and the same guy danced with me, covering my skirt with his hands. The gentle swaying to the music made the wet fabric of my pants rub against my clit, and that and his hands on my bum made me quite turned on. He got even more intimate and I could feel his prick nuzzling against my crotch. He whispered things to me, and I found myself being led upstairs to the bathroom. He made me stand in the bath and then he lifted my skirt and rubbed my crotch through my pants. They were a bit dryer, but I was getting very turned on indeed, and he asked if I had been turned on when I'd wet myself. I said not at first.

Then he asked me to do it again. I relaxed my bladder muscles but found I couldn't do it. In fact I needed a pee again now, but something in my social conditioning was stopping me. He said not to worry, he'd wait till I was absolutely bursting again and then we'd go to the bathroom once more. Within an hour I could hardly stand still, but the bathroom was occupied. I stood there, hopping from leg to leg, holding my crotch until the occupant came out, then I dashed in, discreetly followed by Steve.

I lifted my skirt and stood astride the loo, and as he ran his hands up my legs, I let rip and my pee poured down through my pants. He gently stroked my crotch as I peed, and when I finished he massaged my clit through the wet cotton. My knees kept knocking and banging against the cistern as I gradually lost control on nearing orgasm. Just when I thought I was going to explode he stopped, pulled off my wet knickers and lay me down on the floor. He then dropped his pants and rammed his cock up me. It didn't last long, but it was very satisfying and we both enjoyed the whole episode.

He flushed my pants down the loo, and I spent the rest of the evening with spunk running down my legs and men fondling my knickerless bum as we danced.

I was quite pissed by this time, and apparently I got quite daring later on, by bending over a lot, and doing lots of vigorous twirls in my dances, flashing my naked lower half — but I don't remember much of that!

Since then I've been wetting myself on various occasions. Sometimes in private, sometimes in places where I know people can see me. The last time was at the Ideal Home Exhibition. I got separated from my friend and went to the ladies, only to find a great queue. I stood there for 10 minutes without moving and I could feel the pee seeping through my knickers. I crossed my legs tight, but soon they were saturated, so I walked off and gradually let my pee out as I walked along.

After 5 minutes I'd emptied my bladder and all that was noticeable were my wet socks where the pee had run down my legs. I got so turned on I left my friend there and got the train home, masturbating all the way by swinging one leg over the other. Delightful! Keep up the good work.

Linda, W. London

Bather's Delight

I am 27 and for five years shared my life with a man I hoped to marry. Things went wrong and I left him. Because I had nowhere to go I was very grateful when my cousin Helen took me in.

She and her husband Tom slept in the next room to me, and because it is a modern flat and the walls are very thin, I didn't have to listen very hard to hear them in bed at night. The bed made quite a lot of noise too, and they fucked away every night. There was only one thing I could do and that was to put my hand between my legs and rub myself off.

Helen and Tom could keep going for some time and I frequently had two or three orgasms. Sometimes when I thought they had finished Tom would start up again. They had obviously been lying there with his prick embedded in Helen's hot cunt!

Those two were always fucking. I could even hear them on Saturday and Sunday mornings. Several times on a Sunday I rubbed off in the kitchen as I made coffee. Once I even waited until they had finished and took them in a cup. Helen sat up in bed, obviously naked, and the nipples of her full breasts were sticking out like organ stops.

Then came the evening several girls and myself went for a drink after work. I had to get two buses home, and each time I had a long wait. I began to regret drinking lager and lime, and by the time the second bus arrived I was dying to pee. When I got off the bus there was nowhere to go except home. As I half ran to the flat my bladder felt like a football inside me, and I was nearly wetting myself as I put the key in the lock.

There was a light in the bathroom, but I just couldn't wait. Tom was in the bath, but I was desperate. With my coat unbuttoned, I pulled up my dress and began to yank my panties down. My pee burst from me and I quickly sat on the loo, but not before I had soaked my panties and tights. Tom sat up in the bath and, red faced, all I could do was apologise.

'My God, Anne, you've wet your knickers,' he said. I told him I had nearly done it on the bus. At last I finished and took toilet paper to wipe myself. I did not care that Tom was watching. I felt randy and decided that I had better remove my wet panties and tights. To do this I had to unzip my boots and take them off as well.

When I did finally get up off the loo, naked to the waist under my dress, my pussy was soaking wet. Tom sat in the bath making no attempt to hid his erection. I just stared at it. It was huge.

'What a lovely present you have for Helen.' I said.

'Do you like it?' he asked.

I said I wouldn't mind one like it myself, to which he replied, 'I'm sure you could share it.' I told him that I was sure Helen would object.

'Not if she doesn't know,' said Tom. 'She's round at Mabel's and won't be back for a while.'

He stood up in the bath and asked me to pass him a towel. I helped him to dry off, and a few minutes later I was as naked as himself in my bedroom.

There was no need for any messing around. I was as hot for him as he was for me, and I came as soon as his prick slid into me. With me he did not prolong it, but just shagged away until he came and I came again. We both got dressed and something made me tell him I could hear him and Helen fucking. He asked me if it turned me on and I told him that it did, and that I rubbed off listening to them. 'I think about that when I'm screwing Helen,' he told me.

Tom and I have had several fucks since. Quick ones when Helen is out shopping — more prolonged when she goes for a hair-do. I have also found a new boyfriend and I get a further ration from him in the back of his car. And all because the lady was bursting to pee!

Anne, Essex

Blitz-Site Bliss

Way back in 1950 Betty and I had not long been engaged when I took her to meet an elderly invalid aunt of mine. Betty was twenty and a Catholic. We were both hot for each other, but she would not let me fuck her. We would 'pet heavily', as it was called then, and Betty would not be satisfied until she had come two or three times. She had also taken to habitually wearing french knickers so that I could get at her more easily.

On this particular evening we had to catch two buses each way. On the way back we had rather a long wait for the second bus. Betty became restless and confided to me that she was 'dying for a wee.' We had both drunk rather a lot of tea, and I told her that I also wanted to pee. Eventually the bus came and Betty sat next to me, her legs crossed and her thighs visibly working together under her skirt. I realised that she must be bursting and at once I developed a throbbing hard-on.

Ten minutes later we got off the bus. Betty took my arm. 'Darling, I'm nearly wetting my knickers,' she told me, 'I'll have to find somewhere.' We turned off the main road towards her home. It was late and a moonlit night. 'Can you wait until we get to the bomb site?' I asked. 'I hope so,' she said, 'I nearly did it on the bus.'

She was breathing heavily by the time we reached the bomb site, a place we often went to masturbate each other. As I pulled aside a loose board to allow her access, Betty stood cross-legged, holding herself between her thighs. She stumbled through the opening and stood knock-kneed as she tugged up her skirt with slip. 'I'm doing it,' she wailed, her skirt half way up. She opened her legs, her feet wide apart. I watched as she bent forward a little, one hand struggling to pull skirt and slip higher, the other reaching upwards.

A torrent descended from between her thighs with a loud hiss. Seconds later she was standing legs astride, all stockings and suspenders as she pissed through the leg of her french knickers. 'Oh, but you mustn't look! I can't stop. Please don't look.' But look I did. I unbuttoned my flies and exposed my throbbing erection. Somehow I managed a couple of squirts of pee and then gave up trying.

Betty's flow ebbed away and she had hardly finished but my hand was between her thighs, my free arm around her waist. She was doubly wet with pee and her love juices. 'No, no. With this,' she gasped, and took hold of my prick. She began to rub my knob on her clitoris. Moments later she gasped as I slid part way into her vagina. I began thrusting. 'Don't make me pregnant,' she panted, just as I started to come. I pulled out just in time and my spunk jetted on to her thigh. I replaced it with one and then two fingers, finger-fucking her to several orgasms before she finally reached down and pushed my hand away.

I just had to pee now. As I stood pissing she used my hanky to wipe my spunk from her thigh and stocking top. 'My knickers are wet,' she told me. I said she should take them off and she did, and put them rolled up in her handbag. I put my prick away and Betty put her arms around me. We began to kiss and I fondled her breasts through her blouse. Soon I had her blouse undone and the fingers of one hand inside her bra cup, playing with a stiff nipple. I began to get hard again, and very little persuasion was required to get Betty to allow me to fuck her again, this time with a french letter I had been keeping in my wallet for months!

We often fucked in the privacy of that bomb site — always fully dressed, always standing up. Most times I had to frig her afterwards, as one orgasm did not satisfy her. Betty's dearest wish was for us to be able to do it in bed, but the opportunity never occurred until the following year.

In the meantime there came another occasion when both of us were dying to pee. Late in the year we went blackberry picking in Epping Forest one Sunday. We took a picnic lunch with us. We both had hopes of privacy (and fucking) but other people had the same idea as ourselves.

We picked the blackberries and had our lunch, and then picked more berries. After a while Betty said she needed to pee badly. Again I told her I also needed to pee, and I once more developed a throbbing prick. I had been half-hard with wanting her for some time anyway.

I told Betty to go down the footpath and go behind some bushes. She said she was too shy and that we should go together and find another place. Betty snuggled closer as we left the other berry pickers behind. I reached upwards to fondle her breast. 'I forgot my brassière,' she giggled, and I began to finger her erect nipple. A shiver ran through her. 'You'll make me wet my knickers and they're wet enough already. I just know I'd come if you tried to put your thing in me.' I recalled our visit to aunt Sue and asked if she was as desperate as on that occasion. 'If I don't do it soon, I will be. What about you?' I told her I had such a big horn on I doubted if I could pee, much as I needed to. She giggled, and gasped, 'Ooh! You made me do some.'

At that I led her off the footpath and we made for a coppice. Betty began to hurry a bit, and once within the trees she stopped. She tugged up her dress and slip and pulled down her french knickers. She squatted and I could see her dark pubic bush, from which spurted a hissing golden stream. My prick hardened even more. My balls tightened right up. Strange as it may seem today, that was my first real view of Betty's naked pussy. We had always petted and fucked in the dark of the bomb site. That afternoon we threw caution to the wind in the coppice. She took off both her dress and knickers and I knelt over her, finger-fucking her, watching my fingers go in and out of her slippery vagina. She bared her breasts and I began to suck first one nipple and then the other. Before long my jacket and trousers were off and we were fucking.

We both still remember that afternoon well — Betty half naked beneath me, knees up, thighs spread wide, feet firmly planted on the ground as she churned under me, her arms tight about me, hands gripping me, gasping out

'It's right in me. Oh God! You're stretching me wide open. Do it. Do it harder. I'm coming. I'm coming. Oh, don't stop.'

The next year we married, and in the meantime had to be content with the bomb site. Betty never used a loo if she could help it, and always waited until we were alone to do it standing on the site. Betty is now 52 and looks ten years younger. I still get a hard-on watching her pee, and these days she seems to be able to hold gallons and to pee louder and with more force.

George, Romford

Abide A Wee

A letter praising full-figured older ladies has reminded me of an episode from when I was a young man of barely eighteen.

I was invited to spend a week with a lady called Mary who was a contemporary and friend of my parents.

The afternoon I arrived she was wearing a light grey twin-set and red tartan skirt. Her stockinged legs were strong and shapely. We were in the lounge when she took off the cardigan of her twin-set and stood by the window. As we talked I took in the full beauty of her curvaceous body. I stared at her large, shapely tits in the tight-fitting short-sleeved jumper. Smiling, she looked down her tits and then at me.

'What's so fascinating?' she asked, a mischievous look in her dark brown eyes. "I . . . er . . . like your t-t-tartan skirt", I stammered. Still smiling she said, 'thank you. You must wear your kilt tomorrow.'

The next morning I was awakened by the sound of Mary's bath water running away. I lay day-dreaming, thinking of her big tits in the grey jumper, and I was wanking when she came into the room. She was, as the French say, *déshabillé* — she had on some sort of figure-shaping foundation garment and stockings, over which she wore a salmon-pink slip edged with lace.

'Good morning, Jamie,' she said, pulling the bed clothes off me. 'Into the bathroom with you.'

I slept naked and so, blushing, tried to hide my erection. She followed me into the bathroom where I got into the bath she had run for me, my cock still stubbornly erect. She saw I was trying to hide my penis, and took my hand saying, 'There's no need to be prudish with me!' My proud cock was as defiantly erect as ever.

'Oh you poor lad,' she said, 'It's not good for you to feel frustrated. Stand up.' She soaped her hands and sensitively caressed my lucky prick. 'Ah, you've grown into a fine man Jamie,' she sighed. Again she soaped her hands, and this time began wanking me in earnest.

I was astounded. I had hardly arrived and here I was being wanked off by a bonny, buxom lassie in her underclothes. She was really good at it. The orgasm I had was so sweet and intense, my spunk jetting out and falling into the water. Gently she squeezed the remaining spunk from my prick and left me to finish my bath.

I returned to my bedroom and Mary came in dressed in a red blouse, brown tweed skirt and jacket and low-heeled shoes. As I picked up my underpants she snatched them from me with a laugh, telling me that men shouldn't wear them under kilts.

After breakfast we went for a walk. We'd been walking for an hour or so when she said that she was dying to spend a penny. We stopped and looked around. 'You can go anywhere here,' I said, 'There's no-one to see you is there?'

She turned to face me. 'Except you,' she replied, adding, 'But I don't mind you watching me.' And so saying, she hoisted her skirt and slip up to her waist.

She was clad in silk from waist to toe. Her salmon-pink silk knickers skin-tight to mid-thigh, covering the tops of her silk stockings. She looked sensational and I got a terrific hard-on. She slipped her knickers down to her knees, exposing the voluptuous white curves of her massive arse. Taking off my kilt (no underpants), I knelt beside her and looked up. She pissed for a long while and I was captivated, wanking as I watched her.

When she had finished and was standing up straight I kissed and stroked her soft, plump bum cheeks. When I stroked down the cleft between them she gave an involuntary shiver, went down on all fours and pushed her arse up towards me. I gently parted her and pushed my tongue into her. 'Oh Jamie,' she cried. 'You're wicked, it's wonderful. But not here. Wait until we're home — it's not far.'

Only a few minutes later we were in her bedroom. I was naked by the time she had taken off her jacket, skirt and shoes. She took off her blouse, letting it fall to the floor. She was standing by the bed and beckoned to me. We kissed and she whispered, 'You can take my knickers down now.'

She took off her slip as I knelt in front of her. I eased her knickers down to her knees and saw the majestic swell of her belly curving down to her dark pubic bush, metal suspender clips attached to silk stockings. I stroked her cunt slit. 'Fuck me. Fuck me!' she pleaded, falling back onto the bed, legs spread apart. I pulled her knickers right off, climbed on to her, penis rampant, and for the first time entered her tunnel of love. The sensation was so fantastic that I came almost at once, much to her distress.

But being a young athletic spunk machine I quickly recovered and fucked for a long time. And later it was great, getting off her foundation garment and seeing her giant naked tits. I orgasmed four times that day — now I'm lucky if I can make it four times a week. Ah well — c'est la vie!

J.M., Dundee

5. GOLDEN OLDIES

Daily Helping
Extra Mural Studies
Spanning The Generations
Caravan Capers
Come Into The Garden
Cuddly Love
Whatever Happened To
    Aunt Alice?

Bawd & Lodging
Pigs Can Fly
A Bull By The Horn
Relatively Speaking. . .

Daily Helping

My 'Auntie' Elsie is 54 and quite plump with tits like udders and thighs and arse to match. She isn't my real auntie, just a woman from a nearby village who has been coming in to help my mother around the house for as long as I can remember.

This particular day she was washing the floor, and as she bent down facing me I could see her big tits swinging to and fro. Then she turned round and bent over on her knees. I could see her big fleshy arse and the sight of her nylons, knickers and suspenders gave me the biggest hard on I've ever had and my whole 9″ was throbbing.

I was ready for a real hard wank so I went to my bedroom, lay down and unzipped my trousers. Pulling out my throbbing cock I started a nice slow wank. Then I got the shock of my life when Elsie walked in the room. I had left the door unlocked and I hadn't heard her because she was wearing slippers.

'You naughty boy, Alan,' she exclaimed. 'What do you think you're doing?'

I started to try and explain, but I shut up when she sat on the edge of the bed and reached towards my prick. She began to move her hand up and down my shaft and rolled the flat of her hand around my Bobby's Helmet. This made my prick seem even bigger and harder. She started to wank me off, and as she did so I undid the top button of her overall and felt for her tits. 'Wait a minute, darling,' she said. 'I won't be long. Take all your clothes off. I'll be back soon.'

She was back in less than a minute. Dropping the overall from her shoulders she stood before me stark naked. I have never seen bigger tits or a twat like hers. The hairs were jet black and shaped like a Japanese fan.

I pulled her towards me and kissed her big tits before getting down between her legs to face her hairy twat. My tongue was soon forcing its way between the mass of thick black hairs as I searched for her clitoris. I found it and began giving her a good hard love tittle. She began jerking

156

her arse up and down like mad as I speeded up my tongue movements.

'Oh darling,' she cried out. 'I have never had this before. My old man has never done it. It's lovely . . .'

Then I started to play with her big nipples, which were hard and sticking out like bullets. She started to plead for my big prick then, crying out, 'Give me your prick, please, love. I need it so . . .'

I got up from between her legs and prepared to mount her. She took hold of my throbbing prick and began to rub me up like mad. Then she lifted her legs up in the air and guided my knob into her juicy twat. I could feel the heat of her twat on my knob as she wrapped her big thighs around my body and I dug my nails into the plump flesh of her arse. I began sucking hard on her nipples as I rammed every inch of my big prick up her big hairy cunt.

'It's heaven, darling,' she sighed. 'You're so big. Let it all go, shoot all your spunk inside me. I can't have a baby.'

I shagged away like a sex-starved rabbit, I had never had a 54-year-old woman before. I slowed down for a rest, but she urged me on: 'Come on, shag me harder, shag me good . . .'

At last I could hold out no longer and we must have shot our loads together. When I pulled away her love juices were all over my prick. We lay resting for a while, then she started stroking my prick again. She asked me if I had tried it in the doggy position.

We got down on the carpet and she bent down on her hands and knees, her big fleshy arse towards me. I stroked her damp cunt with my finger, then guided my prick in, giving her the full length with one hard lunge. Reaching over to her udders, I played with her nipples while I rode her like a rampant bull.

She wanted more after that, but I was too knackered. But we had it quite regularly after that occasion: she really satisfied my lust for mature women and she was really grateful to get the spunk of a randy young 25-year-old.

J.C., Lancs.

Extra Mural Studies

Since my experience with a mature lady during my student days in the mid-Sixties, I am a great lover of mature women, I was studying at Leeds University and was staying with a couple as a paying guest.

Mrs D., or Mary as she insisted I call her, was an attractive 42-year-old and her husband was a few years older. Within a short time I became very friendly with them both. Mary's husband was an executive with a big company and Mary was often complaining that he devoted too much time to his work. It was obvious to me that he was neglecting her and her needs.

One evening he was even later returning home than usual. I was in my room, but I could hear Mary restless and sobbing in her room, pacing up and down. Imagine my surprise when not long after, she came into my room. She was obviously upset, and as I tried to comfort her she started to kiss me passionately on the lips.

Then we heard the front door open and she left the room. I heard her have a terrible row with her husband, she screaming at him, and he making excuses for his delayed return.

I spent the following two days in great frustration as I did not know whether there would be a continuation of the incident between Mary and I. Except for the occasional look, she gave me no sign of encouragement.

Anyway, the following weekend we all went together to a charity dance at the local social centre. I was enjoying myself greatly, dancing with Mary and having a few drinks. Then, a short while later, Mary's husband came up and asked me if I would drive Mary home as she wasn't feeling too well.

On the way back Mary and I didn't say much to each other, and once again I was anxious to see what would come next. As we left the car and went into the house Mary gave me an unmistakable wink, and I knew then that I would have her.

Our lips met and our tongues explored each other's

mouths. Then she took me by the hand and led me to her bedroom, where once again we started kissing and fondling each other. We undressed and she fell to her knees and took my knob in her mouth. I was just about to come when I took it gently from her and pushed her back on the carpet, guiding it towards her juicy cunt. She was moaning and kissing me with wild passion as we both climaxed.

I had to leave in a hurry then and return to the dance. Mary's husband asked me what had taken me so long, and I explained that Mary had been sick and I had had to put her to bed and make her a hot drink.

Since that night and until the end of my stay, Mary and I were lovers. She was fantastic and would do anything to please me — though above all I knew she was pleasing herself. She had imagination and was never ashamed to try new positions or create the right atmosphere in our lovemaking, like dressing in dark stockings and high-heels or having a red light on while fucking.

In the meantime her husband got promoted and it led to him travelling abroad quite often. When he was away, Mary and I used to live like husband and wife. She was very fond of 'little games' as she called them. One of them was to kiss passionately on the sofa and then to undress each other on the way to the bedroom, so that by the time we fell onto the bed we were both naked.

But our relationship was not merely sexual. I became quite attached to her and was quite jealous when her husband was at home with her and I could hear them fucking in the next room, in the same bed where a few hours earlier I had been in his position.

At one stage we even thought of running away together, but on second thoughts decided it was not a good idea. I think Mary's husband realised what was going on, but he seemed patient enough to wait until I had finished my studies and left, when our relationship had to end.

T.A., Cyprus

Spanning The Generations

After my divorce I came home to pay a visit to my mother, herself divorced from my father and living with a chap about my own age. In the course of talking we discussed 'Auntie' Vi, a distant relative of my mother, who was now on her own after her husband had left her for a much younger woman. She was 62 and living on her own, and mum suggested I pay her a visit.

I wasn't too keen, until she showed me some old copies of 'Spick' and 'Span' magazines, some thirty years old, that she had carefully kept. I was amazed to see Auntie Vi in photos wearing black stockings, high heels and brief undies. Mum explained that her uncle had taken them of Vi, who was quite a girl in her day.

Auntie Vi was both pleased and surprised to see me. We talked and talked. She admitted she was very lonely and drank too much. I told her that I was divorced, we had sold the house, I had moved into a flat and bought a new car. I stayed with her a week and took her out each night, but she did like her drink. When she had had a few she told me about Reg leaving her, and how she had done everything to please. I mentioned the photos.

She laughed, and said she had nice legs in those days, and pulled up her skirt to show me. 'They are old, like me now, no man would look twice any more,' she said. I looked long and hard. They were still good for her age, clad in dark brown seamed stockings and pink suspenders. On my last night I got the drink and we stayed together curled up on her settee. She got half-drunk and started crying about me leaving her. She had made up her face especially for me, and used the perfume I had bought for her. We kissed and hugged. She said the last week was the happiest she had spent for years. My hand was up her skirt feeling the silky chocolate nylons I had given her, with a new pair of high-heeled black shoes.

She smiled and let my hand move up between her legs and swooned as I worked her off. 'No man has done that for a long time.' she said. 'Vi!' I blurted out, 'I want to fuck you.'

My swollen prick was in her warm old hands. She said, with a sparkle in her eyes, 'I want to be fucked and fucked!'

A month later 'Auntie' Vi moved into my new flat, and now she looks after me like a mother. She has promised to do everything I ask of her. Her hair has been dyed blonde, she wears heavy make-up, false eyelashes and long red nails. I have bought her new silk and nylon undies, new short dresses and skirts. She has practised in the flat wearing the very high-heeled shoes I bought. She is over the moon with happiness, and despite her age, never refuses my stiff 9″ cock shooting hot spunk inside her. 'Your semen makes me young,' she laughs.

We paid a visit to my mother who was very surprised, but delighted to see us both so happy. She gave us the copies of 'Spick' and 'Span'. Vi has promised me to pose again in exactly the same way, and we would both love to see the photos in Fiesta, which is our favourite magazine. You would never guess she was 62 years of age.

Dave, Devizes

Caravan Capers

My first experience with a mature woman came when I was 19, naive, but still curious about sex. My cousin owned a caravan at the seaside and he was always telling me to drop in and stay anytime I liked. And that is just what I did.

I arrived there unannounced, expecting to find nobody there as both my cousin and Diane, his wife, go out to work. But I was surprised to find Diane sitting outside the caravan having a cup of coffee in the sunshine.

She came into the caravan with me and helped me to unpack my suitcase. She said that she was quite pleased to see me as she was off work with a stomach disorder and I could help with odd chores around the site. I waited while she changed in the bedroom, and then we walked down to the village to buy some groceries.

During the walk we made idle chat and she asked me if I had any girlfriends, to which I replied no. I was quite turned on by her prying questions about my non-existent sex life, so that it was no surprise to me that I returned to the caravan with a strong erection.

After we had packed away the groceries, Diane asked me outright how far I had gone with any girl. I was quite embarrassed, but I answered truthfully that I had never touched a girl's body, apart from the odd kiss. She asked if it was because I didn't want to, or because I never had the chance, and I told her it was the latter reason.

At this, Diane stood up, took my hand and led me through to the bedroom. My heart was pounding. It was a rather small bedroom, but this did not hinder her. She walked across to the bed, grabbed the hem of her summer dress and pulled it up over her head. I thought I was going to pass out as she revealed a pink bra and suspender-belt with matching pink panties.

I unbuttoned my shirt and took off my socks and trousers, standing there in my underpants which did nothing to hide my throbbing erection. Diane unhooked her bra very slowly, teasing me as she did so.

Then she lay on the bed. I pulled off her panties and she told me to lick her cunt. I ripped off my underpants and got on the bed beside her, licking and sucking at her moist slit. The stockings and suspender-belt were really turning me on, as well as her frequent use of swear words.

I could stand it no more and, assuring she had taken precautions, I rammed my cock into her, coming immediately. But she begged me not to stop, so I continued to grind away until she shuddered and motioned me for a break.

I pulled out of her dripping cunt and began sucking on her tits. I was so aroused that my prick stiffened again and we were soon fucking away in other positions.

We screwed every day of that wonderful week while my

162

cousin was at work. When she returned to work herself, I returned home. She lives in Canada now, so there has never been a chance to repeat the experience. But the mature woman, suspenders and all, has won a place in my fantasies for ever.

Frank, Devon

Come Into The Garden

I really enjoyed Fiesta Vol 15 No 7 and the Holiday Special as they included letters and photos of my three favourite subjects — mature, big-breasted women, slips and Directoire knickers, and the occasional male pleasure of wearing women's knickers.

I was once miraculously able to combine all three pleasures. At the time, my wife and I were living in the country in one of two bungalows situated in a secluded spot. The two adjoining gardens were surrounded by high hedges, beyond which were fields.

Our neighbours were a middle-aged couple and we were invited to dinner to celebrate the lady's 55th birthday. Her name was Helen and she had obviously been a beauty when young and she still retained her good looks, though her hair was a little grey and she admitted she'd put on weight.

After dinner I went to the kitchen with her on the pretext of helping with the coffee. In the kitchen we kissed and she let me feel her tits through her blue silk dress. I slid down the straps of her dress and bra and her fat wobbling tits tumbled out, plump and pendulous, the pale pink nipples erect.

Then she backed off, giggling. 'Enough,' she cried, but she proudly displayed her tits, enjoying the admiration she was getting. Eventually she pulled up her dress and bra strap and I had to help her in with the coffee.

I just had to get at her tits again, so I took the next week off work. I knew she would be at home alone and that my wife was at work all day. It was a hot, still summer day. I had seen Helen in the morning and she had invited me across to lunch.

About mid-day Helen came into her garden to take in her washing. I was working in mine. I was pleased to see from the washing on the line that her knickers were of the Directoire style. I joked with her about her knickers being old-fashioned, but secretly, of course, I liked them and thought they suited her mature image.

It was so hot and sunny that she had taken off her dress. Her silky white slip and the outline of her substantial bra were turning me on like mad. I indulged my slip fetish to the full, ogling her up and down, and I'm sure she noticed my hard-on.

I went in to change for dinner. I got a couple of bottles of wine from the fridge, had a quick shower, then put on a pair of white nylon elastic briefs which would pass as swimming trunks but for the bands of elastic around the waist and legs.

She had set our salad lunch in the garden. Straightaway she noticed my pants and commented favourably on them. After our meal and a few glasses of wine each we were sitting together on the lawn and she began to wank me skilfully through the knickers until I orgasmed.

'Now you'll have to wear a pair of mine,' she said, 'Get those off.'

We went inside and she washed and towelled my cock and balls and handed me a pair of her Directoires to put on. I was partly amused, but excited by the idea that she wanted to see me in them, so I obeyed.

'Keep them,' she said. 'And whenever you wear them, think of me.'

The wine had really reached my head now and I could see her knickers up her slip and feel the caress of silky nylon on my rising prick.

'We could sunbathe naked outside and no one would see us,' she remarked. So I slipped off the knickers and she stared hungrily at my proud and erect penis as she

164

took off her own underwear. Her tits looked bigger than I remembered them.

Outside on the lawn we lay down and she took my cock in her mouth and began to suck me expertly. Then I happened to glance up at the bungalow and saw a shadowy figure behind the curtains. Someone was watching us! She stopped sucking my cock long enough to say, 'I told my husband you fancied me — he wanted to watch.'

I looked again towards the bungalow and made out the figure I recognised now as her husband. He was naked and wanking. They had planned it!

I just relaxed as best I could after that and she worked my cock with her mouth until it was hard as iron. I fucked her there on the lawn with her husband watching. Then we changed position and I lay on my back while she rode me, her gigantic tits quivering just above my face.

'My husband likes me to do this,' she said, lifting a tit to her mouth and sucking her own nipple, leaning forward so that her other tit flopped onto my face where I sucked and licked at it until my spunk exploded inside her.

We gave her husband several shows that week, and I enjoyed it as much as I'm sure he did.

J.E., Avon

Cuddly Love

I must congratulate you on providing me with the woman of my dreams — I refer of course to Corinne of Kent, Vol. 17 No. 11. She has everything that I ever fantasise about. That arse of hers is so inviting that I've wanked myself silly over her. I hope you carry on showing us more mature women in the near future.

Which prompts me to tell you about the experience I had with such a woman. I'm twenty-four and live with my mother, sister and brother. Karen, an old friend of my mother, moved in with us a couple of years ago when my Dad left us. I have always had a crush on her, and I was pleased when she came to stay. She is around forty-five, single, and for as long as I can remember she has never had a boyfriend.

One day I was in the bath when there was a knock on the door. I called out that I was in the bath, but would be out in ten minutes. It was Karen at the door and she said that she was desperate for a pee and couldn't wait. She opened the door, came in, looked over to me, went straight over to the toilet, pulled her knickers down and had a pee. I didn't know where to look, but glanced over to her and caught sight of her massive arse and even got a flash of her dark hairy cunt.

Before I knew it she got up and left, and as you can imagine I wanked myself silly in the bath.

A few weeks later my mother announced that everyone was going away for the weekend to visit an aunt and uncle, but I told her that I had already arranged to stay with a mate for the Friday evening, and wouldn't be coming. I arranged to see the rest of the family on Sunday when they returned, and went to stay with my pal.

I came home about two o'clock on the Saturday afternoon, expecting to have the house to myself. I opened the front door and went into the hall, and quietly went upstairs to change. On the way up I could hear a low moaning sound. As I got to the landing I realised that the sounds were coming from Karen's room. The door was slightly open and I went over to take a look.

I saw her spread out on the bed, naked, with one hand rubbing her cunt and the other playing with one of her massive tits. I opened the door and walked in. Without saying a word, I bent down and took one of her big brown nipples in my mouth and moved my hand down between her big fleshy thighs and began playing with her clitty. Karen told me to take my clothes off quickly and give her a good fucking — and I was happy to oblige.

It was beautiful to see her huge hairy cunt, juicy and inviting. I slowly parted her legs and went down between her thighs. As I licked her she brought her thighs

166

together, trapping the sides of my head in her warm flesh. She begged me to fuck her and as I got into position between her legs she pulled me down on top of her, kissing me passionately on the mouth.

She took my prick in her hand and guided me into her moist love tube. As I sank into those rolls of flesh I couldn't control myself and came with a mighty spurt. Lying on the bed, I relaxed for a while. Karen began kissing my nipples and then worked her way down to my limp prick. With one sudden gulp she had my balls in her mouth, massaging my prick with one hand as she licked and sucked on my nuts.

My prick was soon standing up firm again with this attention, and we moved round into a sixty-nine position. As Karen lowered her massive arse onto my face, I grabbed hold of it and pulled it towards me. She began to wriggle and moan as I pushed my tongue deep into her slit, and then she got off me and told me to fuck her properly from behind.

I slid my prick into that inviting cunt, grabbing handfuls of her majestic tits as they dangled down in front of her and soon we shuddered to a momentous climax together. Later that evening we repeated our performance, and we take every opportunity we can to make love. I hope you print this letter, because Karen has bet me a blow job that you won't — and I'd love to claim my reward!

Len, Bromsgrove

Whatever Happened To Aunt Alice?

Can you imagine my shock when I opened the page of Fiesta Vol 17 Number 1 and saw the delectable Jackie of London? You see she is the spitting image of my landlady Alice as she was twelve years ago, when I was studying for my A levels. My eyes nearly popped out of my head as the memories came flooding back to me of the most exciting time I have ever had with a woman, despite the fact that I am now married with children of my own.

You see, Alice's husband was a long distance lorry driver, and while he was absent she used to allow me to study at her home so that I could avoid the noise and rumpus my younger brother and sister made at my parent's house.

Anyway one evening while sitting at her table with my books open, she gave me a cup of coffee, and after drinking it I began to feel quite restless and was quite unable to study. Seeing me fidgeting about, Alice suggested I take a break and sit with her at the fireplace. This I did. I sat right opposite her and immediately my eyes were caught by the way in which she was sitting.

Her legs were wide apart and her skirt drawn tautly across her lap, affording me a magnificent view of her nylon clad thighs and her pale pink satiny knickers above the stocking tops. My prick pulsed as I looked with a horny gaze at the wonderful sight before me. She was plump, like Jackie, and had the same soft facial features. My horn grew and grew as I imagined touching her in her crevice, deep in the gorgeous flesh of her ample thighs. Her stockings gleamed and sheened in the light; so very sexy.

I saw her look at the huge bulge in my trousers and realised with a pleasant shock that she now knew that I had a raging horn on. To tease me further she sat up and hitched her skirt higher up her legs, so that it rode well above her gleaming knees. For some reason I felt bold, and I asked her if I could come and sit by her. She agreed and suggested that I sit on the carpet in front of her. So I got up with my horn preceding me and sat with my back to her, on the carpet with my head resting on her skirt, and my arms over her legs. The feel of the nylon on my bare arms sent thrills of anticipation through me, for I realised that she too was feeling randy, or she would never have sat as she did or allowed me to sit between her legs.

As I leaned back her skirt slipped higher and higher up her thighs under the pressure of my shoulders, until her thighs were fleshily astride me. I felt her hands fiddling with her skirt and the next thing I knew was that she was pressing my head into the warm soft crotch of her knicks and she was stroking me into her.

She leaned forward and her large tits pressured against my cheeks, while her hands slipped down to my fly and started to undo my buttons. The feel of her silken knicker gusset on the nape of my neck forced the hot blood even harder up my prick so that I had a horn on like I had never experienced before.

Alice took my prick out, and commented upon the size for a lad of my age, as she fondled and caressed it, rolling my purple knob to its full extent. I groaned as she rubbed it up and down in her soft, fat, smooth hands, until unable to hold it any longer I arched my back and she guided my spunk into the fire grate where it hissed on the hot bars. I spurted and spurted until I felt quite empty. Then she wiped it with a tissue which was at her side.

Panting, I turned towards her and buried my face into her knickers, kissing and sucking at her wet knicker gusset. She leaned back in her chair and with one hand she pulled aside one of the panty legs, and there before me was her gaping beautiful cunt, covered in a thick layer of pubic curls. I rested my arms on her thighs and using my fingers I parted the luxuriant growth and buried my tongue into her secret depths, scooping greedily at the dewlap of her sex.

I stroked her cunt lips with the tip of my tongue from anus to clitoris, a full six inches, then using the tip I ran over and round the little nodule of her clit. It was her turn to arch her back and after a while she began to wriggle and writhe as she got closer to reaching a climax. When she did she clamped her thighs round my face and all that lovely flesh very nearly suffocated me, but I managed to keep breathing until she suddenly went limp.

By this time my prick had risen to another raging horn, and all I wanted to do was to shag this delicious fleshy landlady of mine. I was so eager that I crawled up her body and tried to put my prick in there, but all I could manage was a touch of her outer lips. Alice pushed me away, and taking my hand in hers she led me upstairs to the main bedroom.

Off came her blouse and skirt and there she stood, her great tits held tightly in a satin bra, her wide suspender belt-come-corset, overlaying her sexy knickers and the straps holding her stockings up stretched as tight as could be. She undid the fastening on the belt and let it fall to the carpet and her flesh fell into rolls of exquisite delight. Off came her bra and her tits dropped into their natural position with nipples like stair rods protruding from the rounded fleshy melons.

Without taking my eyes off her I quickly stripped and held out my stiff rigid prick for her to see. She advanced on me, her legs trembling just as much as mine. She slipped out of her knickers, strangely keeping her stockings on, held up by the tightly gripping tops.

Laying back on the bed she invited me with her eyes to mount her and, with her legs wide as could be, I got between those thundering thighs. She guided my prick right deeply into her moist cunt. Her cunt lips gripping me as I shagged away, kneading her tits and flesh all the while. Her arse fell into rhythm with my movements and as we had already come once we managed to prolong the gorgeous fuck for quite a time. Each thrust and response thrilled us both with wonderful sensations. Then we came, in a tangle of flesh and movement, our mouths glued together and eyes closed in pure heaven.

Three times more we shagged that evening, before I had to go, but from then on my studies were interspersed with shagging Alice, and it was a long time before she told me that she had slipped a tiny drop of benzedrine in my coffee, which had made me feel so bold toward her, and enhanced my shagging.

I cannot get over the resemblance between her and Jackie, I've already masturbated several times looking at her pictures and remembering those wonderful occasions.

Viv, Cardiff

Bawd And Lodging

When I was in digs back in 1967 my landlady was a pleasant sort of woman of about 44. I was only 21 then and fancied her a lot. She was a lovely bundle of fun with large boobs and very shapely legs.

She was a widower and her two children had left home some time ago. She asked me one day if my parents would mind me living with a widow, but I told her not to worry as they were unlikely to find out. I had told them that my digs were good — and I told the landlady I wanted to stay and she seemed very pleased.

She was just my cup of tea. She always wore seamed nylons, and also a lot of see-through blouses which showed off her lovely tits and lovely brassieres.

One day I walked into the bathroom and she was bent over the washbasin washing her hair. She had a white long-line bra on and as her skirt was quite short I could see her stocking-tops at the back. I had a hard-on straight away, but apologised for intruding.

She looked round and wrapped the towel around her wet hair. 'I'm not shy,' she said. 'I've got my bra on, it's just the same as a bikini, isn't it?'

'Well it's a bit see-through,' I said as I stared at her huge cleavage and the big aureolae which must have been 3″ across.

'Well as long as that's all you see, there's no harm done, is there?' she said to me.

I blushed and before I knew what I was doing I blurted out, 'And I could see your stocking-tops when you bent over.'

'Yes, I know my skirt's a bit short,' she admitted. 'Did you enjoy the view?'

'It was wonderful,' I said.

Looking at me out of the corner of her eye, she suddenly realised I was quite serious.

Nothing happened then, but I began to have hopes that I could get somewhere in the next few days. Sure enough, another opportunity came a few nights later, while she was doing the ironing.

She picked up a pair of underpants which I'd had given me, which had the slogan *I'm Thick* on them. They were not the Y-front type and were difficult to pee in. She laughed and held them up.

'I ask myself two questions,' she said. 'How on earth do you get in them, and, are you what it says?'

'I only wear them when I get a bit low on clean ones,' I said. 'They're a bit tight.' And I added, 'But you can talk. How do you get in these?' I held up a pair of very brief panties, which were white and virtually see-through. My throat was tight and dry and I wondered what she would say next.

'These stretch more than yours,' she said. 'Anyway, I'm not too fat, am I?'

'No, you're just right,' I assured her. 'But I'd love to see them on. . .'

'Alright,' she said. 'But I want to see yours on as well. You go and put them on in the bedroom, I'll put mine on in here — then we'll both walk into the lounge from different doors. . .'

So we did just that. She looked fantastic. All she had on was the large bra and her tiny white panties. I had a real hard-on and my knob was right up to the waistband of my pants.

I looked at her hairy crotch. The hair showed through the white material, grew up to her tummy, and curled out from the knicker legs. 'God, you're hairy, aren't you?'

'I've always been hairy. I think it's sexy, don't you?'

'Fantastic,' I agreed.

She stared at my bulging pants. 'I can't stop myself,' she said. 'I'm going to feel him.' She held out her hand and squeezed my cock through my pants. 'Isn't he lovely and thick? Can I hold him for a bit?'

I nodded. 'But I might come and make a mess,' I warned her.

She pulled down my pants and exposed my rampant cock. 'You might come? Well, I'm going to make sure I

172

do. Excuse me while I have a wank, will you?'

She plunged her other hand into her panties and parted her legs, wanking herself to orgasm in about two minutes. She made an awful lot of noise, but when she came it was fantastic.

When she had finished she hugged me. 'I needed that so much,' she said. 'I was so frustrated. Would you like me to give you a wank as well?'

'If you really want to know,' I said, 'I'd like you to go and get completely dressed as if we were going out tonight.'

'Oh, Jim, I'm sorry if I upset you . . .' she apologised.

I cut her off and explained that I wanted her to do a striptease for me, to which she eagerly agreed. I fondled my prick while she was getting ready, but I was careful not to go too far.

'What do you want me to do now?' she asked when she reappeared. 'I'm completely in your hands.'

'Just undo your blouse and show a bit of cleavage and your brassiere,' I told her. 'And cross your legs carelessly so that I can see your stocking-tops and suspenders.'

This she did, and I carried on enjoying a wonderful slow wank. Then I told her to play with her titties, and she took both her breasts out and began playing with the nipples until they were huge.

'Are you close to coming yet?' she asked. 'Because I may get carried away again . . .'

'Not yet,' I begged her. 'Leave your suspender-belt on.'

'Yes, I thought that's what you wanted to see,' she said. She stripped down to her suspenders then, and I fondled her great big tits while wanking myself with my other hand. 'I feel randy again myself,' she said. 'What about us wanking each other?'

So that's just what we did. It was fantastic, though we agreed not to have intercourse, but just to wank each other off.

'Anytime you get the horn,' she said to me. 'Just get him out and have a wank if you want to. And if I fancy one

I'll do the same.'

So now you kow why I'm still single and I've been in the same digs for the past fourteen years. . .

J.K., Powys

Pigs Can Fly

I am a 31-year-old married man, and I've always wanted to screw a much older woman in a piggery. One day I met such a woman in my local. She is 49-years-old, and I had seen her many times before with her husband, but this time she was on her own.

I walked past her table and accidently-on-purpose knocked over her drink, my aim being to buy her another. After I had apologised and bought her another drink, we got chatting.

She told me that her husband was away on a business trip. All the time I kept mentally undressing her, and I was so worked up that after a few more drinks I found myself becoming obscene. I told her I would dearly like to screw her and that my balls were aching with the desire to abuse her.

She must have thought I was joking. 'And just where do you want to do it?' she asked. 'Right here? In my car? Or in my own bed?'

When I told her I had a fantasy about screwing her in a piggery and that no other place would do, she seemed quite surprised. But to my own surprise, she agreed.

Once in her car, we drove straight to a farm I knew of where there was a pig-pen. We left the car in a hidden driveway and walked hand in hand to the pig-pen. We both stripped off, and for a woman of 49 she had a good firm pair of tits, a wide arse and soft belly, and in the moonlight she looked so inviting.

Naked, we shared the area of slush-like mud and pig shit with four pigs. The swampy ground came up to our shins. She seemed to like the idea and she soon started

174

throwing pig-shit at me. I joined in the game, and there we were, rolling about in the shit, enjoying every second, and our only witnesses four bewildered pigs.

I managed to get her in a doggy position and shagged the arse off her, making her squeal like a pig as she climaxed to a shuddering end. I then had her on her back, and then in a 69 position. With the taste of her fanny juice there was a strong smell of pig-shit. She seemed to swallow my big 8″ cock, and I came soon after she did.

Then we drove home, and after showering we spent the night together. For my breakfast I ate a banana which she had pushed up her sweet smelling hole. Then she covered my stiff prick with cream and gobbled it eagerly — getting more cream than she bargained for!

A.C., Scotland

A Bull By The Horn

I am a 52 year old widow, but I manage a fairly active sex life by having an affair with the son of one of my friends, a 23 year old called David. My colleagues and friends imagine that I am 'past it', and in fact I give the impression of being rather severe and frigid. But I have always been highly sexed and easily roused, and it is pleasing to note that some of your readers appreciate more mature women.

Despite my years I try to dress smartly, and on away trips I try to 'let my hair down' a bit. Although you mostly feature slim young girls in your picture sections, I find that many men prefer a fuller figure. I am 5′4″ tall and weigh in at 10st 8lbs. My bust is 44C, waist 28 and I have 40″ hips.

I seduced David approximately four months after my husband died. He was eighteen then and I was 47. He was obviously attracted by my rather heavy bust, and when he visited me one evening I teased him by not wearing a bra. He noticed my omission fairly quickly, and it was obvious while we were preparing supper that he made a few attempts at brushing his hands against my blouse.

His excitement was apparent by the bulge in his trousers, and so taking the bull by the horns I asked him bluntly if he would like to feel them properly. Within minutes we had both stripped, but not before I had sworn him to absolute secrecy. Since that night David has visited me twice a week, during which time I have given him a wonderful sex education.

I find the sight of a rampant naked youth most invigorating, and at his age it is not difficult for him to maintain a gorgeous erection for hours on end. We have enjoyed all forms of sex including 'soixante-neuf', and sucking him is a most beautfiul experience. The sensation of having a vibrant young prick in your mouth is beyond belief. At my suggestion David keeps his balls well shaved, and the feel of smooth naked balls is wonderful. I especially enjoy having his balls in my mouth, now that they are shaved smooth.

David loves to ride me doggy fashion, particularly in front of my full-length bedroom mirror. When I kneel in this position my boobs appear massive and they swing in unison with his thrusts. David is now beginning to control his erections, and can now remain soft when I am naked. The other night after a hot session we had a shower. After the shower I was sitting in my armchair when he entered the room. Both of us were still undressed, and he walked over to me and offered his limp prick to my lips. I opened my mouth and took it all in — about four inches — and it started to grow until my mouth was completely filled. I stretched my head back until I felt its head reaching right into my throat. He rode my mouth, expelling his spunk deep into my throat.

Ours is an unusual relationship, but I am sure it is one which will be envied by many of your older readers. My advice is: don't let people convince you that you are past it. Enjoy whatever turns you on and experiment. To the young men I would say: forget your age and never be afraid of your inexperience. I am sure there are many frustrated older women who would welcome your company.

Joycelyn, Oxon.

Relatively Speaking . . .

Last Christmas Eve my wife and I were putting the finishing touches to the kids' presents under the tree, and were just thinking of turning in for the night when her aunt and uncle popped in for a coffee, as they had been visiting friends down the road from us.

As we sat with the coffee, I was trying to keep myself decent as I was wearing my dressing gown and nothing else. Ruby, my wife's aunt, made a number of comments on my sexy legs. I paid little attention to her comments, as I think my legs are no different to any other fella's, but wondered if I might be in for a treat sometime in the future if I played my cards right.

Ruby is in her mid-forties, with the sort of build I like best of all in a woman — she's not fat but is solidly built with beautifully full boobs. In fact when I returned to work on the rigs, 'Auntie' Ruby became the object of my wanking fantasies.

When I was next on leave, I dropped my wife at the office one morning and decided to put my theory about Ruby to the test. I called round at her house on the pretext of claiming the cup of coffee I was owed from Christmas Eve. By the time I knocked on Ruby's door my legs were shaking with excitement and my Y-fronts were already damp with come which had seeped from my cock.

After Ruby had made the coffee, we sat on the sofa chatting and the subject turned to my 'sexy' legs. I was ready to try my luck this time and I replied that they were nothing compared to hers and that she must have looked a knockout in the mini skirt era. I said that it was a pity that she was wearing trousers, or my point would have been proved.

Ruby was a bit taken aback and I wondered if I had pushed my luck too soon as she blushed a bit. Then she said that if I wasn't in a hurry she could soon change into a dress and I could make up my mind.

I gave her a five minute start after she had gone upstairs, then I crept up after her, took a deep breath and walked into her bedroom saying, 'Is it OK to use the toi. . .' I was rendered speechless. There before me was the object of my lust and desire wearing bra, pants and suspenders and smokey grey nylons, holding the dress that she was about to put on in front of her. She looked so desirable that my legs nearly buckled as I closed the door behind me.

'Don't hide yourself Ruby,' I said, 'You look fantastic — let me see you.' By this time I had moved across the room towards her and I reached out slowly and took the dress from her and laid it on the bed. Stepping back I said she was aptly named — for she was a jewel. Trailing my fingers down her shoulderblade, I unhooked her bra. Ruby gasped as I bent my head to take her nipple in my mouth. Then I ran my hand down her stomach and into the waistband of her knickers, down through a mass of hair until I found her sopping wet hole.

I rotated my finger in the warm wet area I was soon to enter even more intimately, and I lifted my head from her rock hard nipple and fastened my lips to hers. Our tongues entwined and she fumbled with my trouser zip. In a trice my trousers and underpants were around my ankles and she had hold of my rigid cock.

Sinking to her knees in front of me, Ruby ran her tongue down my front and drew my cock into her mouth. It was a glorious sensation as her mouth began to work like a suction pump over the end of my cock. I tried to pull back, but her hands were digging into my buttocks and she continued to suck furiously as I exploded in her mouth. She looked up at me with a smile and said: 'Now let's go to bed.'

We stripped and lay on the bed together, her fingers

gently scratching the underside of my cock and balls, and I played gently with her clitoris. After about ten minutes of this I rolled over between her legs and slid my hands under the cheeks of her bum to raise her fanny to my lips.

What a sight. Her patch was almost a perfect triangle of near jet-black hair and her slit a neat pink gash glistening with moisture around the lips. I began to tease her clit, darting my tongue in and out and sucking and blowing until she arched her back in ecstasy. I moved up until my cock was brushing the entrance to her love tube and moaning, she grasped it with both hands and guided me home. I fucked her slowly until her moans told me her orgasm was approaching and with ever quickening strokes I pushed her over the edge into her climax. I felt my juices rising and in a final thrust shot my semen deep into her as we climaxed together in a shuddering unison.

Afterwards we lay in each others arms discussing what had happened and agreed that we would be hurting no one by keeping it in the family so to speak. She's bored in the house all day and I get fed up on my own on my fourteen days leave. But not any more!

Ken, Aberdeen

6. HOLDING YOUR OWN

Fields Of Fantasy
Special Attachment
Artistic Endeavours
More Pipe Dreams
The Sin Of Donan
Youth Opportunities
Strictly Vegetarian
Slot Metered
Reflects Action
Look, No Hands
Finger Pickin' Blues

Swimmers' Strokes
It Takes One To Tango
Getting It Taped
Homes And Gardeners
A Warm Hand . . .
. . . And Sticky Fingers
Called To The Bra
Strange Bedfellows
Handy With Mandy
Solo Sessions

Fields Of Fantasy

I thought it would be nice to write and tell you of an experience which happened to me last summer. I am 26 years old and I was out cycling one day along a lonely road when I stopped for a smoke. Going into a field, I was just about to settle down, when from the corner of my eye I saw a naked — yes, bollock naked — female of about forty years, lying on her back getting an all-over tan.

Well, when I saw this my cock lurched in my pants and it was very hard within seconds. I thought to myself how much I would love to screw this lovely mature female and, taking my cock from my pants, I stood beside a tree and, while watching the beautiful naked lady, I proceeded to wank my stiff cock.

She seemed to be pretty restless, moving about an awful lot, opening and closing her legs, and I was getting lots of lovely flashes of her hairy pussy. Then the next thing was she was rubbing her hands all over her big brown saggy tits, and I stopped wanking at this point, as I was on the verge of coming.

Her left hand slowly slid down her body and through her pubic hairs until she reached her pussy. Spreading her legs, she slowly inserted first one and then two fingers into her open cunt, which must have been very wet, judging by the way she shoved her fingers in and out. My cock was twitching away like mad, and I was just dying to sink my hard cock into her cunt, but I was rooted to the spot — not wanting to move in case I disturbed her. Still standing there watching, I again started to wank myself.

She removed her fingers from her cunt and began licking and sucking them, while her other hand was now busy fingering her clit. It was moving really fast, and her legs were opening and closing slightly. She moved her hand down from her mouth and onto her tit, where she started to tweak at her erect nipple. All the while her head was tossing slowly from side to side, moaning and gasping as if she couldn't get her breath.

I knew she was about to come, for her hand began to move even faster as she fingered her clit. Then it happened. With a low groan, and all the tossing about she was doing, she came, and so did I. My load left my cock in an arc, landing on a tree in front of me, my last drops landing on my hand. I cleaned myself up with a handkerchief and turned back to where she was lying, but she had gone.

As I was slowly riding along on my bike, a red car passed by slowly and the driver leaned out of the window and said, 'I hope you liked my little act.' I nearly fell off my bike. She was even lovelier close up, and her voice was very sexy. It has always been a fantasy of mine to screw a mature woman like this, and I can only hope she uses that field again.

D., Belfast

Special Attachment
I was interested to read the letter from A.B.S. of Staffs. in Vol. 17 No. 11 about the ways of masturbating. I have a few special ways of my own, and enjoy them very much.

First, I will explain I am a single fellow living in lodgings, and the landlady insists that we keep our rooms tidy. So one Saturday afternoon I asked her if I could use the vacuum cleaner as the other lodgers were out and it was quiet, so I thought it was the best time to clean my room.

I had tidied up and was looking through Fiesta when I had the urge to have a wank. I put a small brush attachment onto the vacuum cleaner and held this over the end of my dick and switched on. It was a lovely feeling when it started sucking my foreskin, making it vibrate, and I lay on my bed having a wonderful time, trying to make it last as long as I could.

What I didn't hear was the landlady coming into my room, as I was enjoying it so much. She just stood by my bed and watched me. Then, when I had finished and I saw her I didn't know what to do or say. She just gave me a new dust bag for the cleaner, smiled and walked out.

When she comes to wake me in the mornings nowadays she knocks on my door before coming in — which she never used to do. One Wednesday morning I was having a wank when she knocked, and as I wanted her to catch me again, I didn't answer her knowing she would come in. I pulled the sheets back and lay there, wanking away with a towel ready. I came my load when she opened the door and she came in and sat on the bed.

She said she had seen it all before, and asked me why I didn't find myself a girlfriend, as she was too old for it now. I asked her to rub me off as I was feeling very randy, so she gave me a wank, then she left.

Dave, Exeter

Readers should note that messing around with vacuum cleaners can cause serious injuries — Ed.

Artistic Endeavours

I was getting things ready to paint the skirting board, whilst decorating the lounge. This gave me an idea.

I bought a new 1″ brush and now I 'brush' or 'paint' my prick! The build up is slow and agonising, and my spunk absolutely flies when I come.

Terry, S. London

More Pipe Dreams
In reply to DIY of Nottingham's letter (Vol. 16 No. 10) about using a length of piping to wank with, I tried this method and found it quite effective and stimulating. But of experimenting with this idea I found it most enhancing to the experience to glue a piece of fur to the end of the pipe. This does two things — it tickles your balls and it keeps the entrance to the tube from scratching your nuts.

T.H., Sunderland

The Sin Of Donan
The letters from D.G. and Phil which appeared in Fiesta Vol. 17 No. 10 prompt me to write to you myself. Like D.G. and Phil I am dedicated to the art of masturbation. Whilst many people masturbate because of lack of sexual contacts, it does not seem to be widely appreciated that a sizeable group prefer masturbation for its own sake. Only a dedicated practitioner can know the peaks of ecstasy which can be reached through self-stimulation.

I have been masturbating for most of my adult life. I am now 41 and in excellent physical shape and do not appear to have suffered from the practice of 'Solitary Vice.' Like Phil I can take myself in hand for lengthy sessions. I detest a 'Rush Job' and, instead, I plan my sessions in detail. I read pornography, listen to sexy tapes, (some made by me!) and remove all my pubic hair to achieve greater sensitivity. I like to observe my activities in well placed mirrors, delighting at the sight of my 7" erection from all angles.

I quite literally have scores of masturbation techniques acquired by experimentation over the years. Each has its own special delights and advantages. However, solo sex has one disadvantage — it is rather frustrating in not being able to communicate one's interests to fellow enthusiasts. I have been tempted to try to contact other masturbators by placing a discreet advert in the personal column of our local evening paper, but never had the courage. It would be nice to contact other clean, discreet enthusiasts to share experiences. The next best thing, I suppose, is to read the letters in Fiesta.

Donan, Belfast

Youth Opportunities
Since my husband and I began to take Fiesta regularly about five years ago, I have become increasingly interested in the masturbatory activities of young male virgins. My part time appointment at a youth club for the past three years has reinforced this interest, and is one of the principal items of gossip between myself and a female organiser at the club. An incident early in my appointment caused increased discussion and investigation.

Whilst in charge of a party at a holiday camp, I and my colleague saw a youth enter his chalet, tear some pictures out of a girlie magazine, place them carefully on his bed and begin to masturbate furiously over them. I was astonished at the amount of pleasure the youth obviously got by looking at pictures.

At the club I am able to pick up information in all sorts of ways, and I now know that certain youths are more predisposed to wank than others. It is nearly always the shy ones who are to be found in the toilets with a girlie magazine in one hand and their penis in the other.

One evening I noticed that one of the nicer and shyer youths, Graham, who I happen to know is an inveterate wanker, was looking up my dress as I sat at my desk. As I quite liked the lad, I could not resist moving my legs about in order to give him a better view, and by casual glances I could see that he was becoming increasingly excited at what he saw.

After a while he disappeared into the toilets. Shortly after, another youth came out and casually remarked to my colleague that, 'Graham is pulling his pud again.' I became very wet between the legs after this, as I was sure that he was thinking about me while he was wanking. Since that time I have flashed to other youths, but do not at the club, because I do not want to get a reputation for doing so.

However, I know from the gossip the tremendous intense pleasure that the youths get from wanking while they look at girlie pictures, and, by the way, Fiesta seems to be the most popular for this purpose. From the knowledge that I have built up, I can confidently tell my husband which picture in Fiesta will get the most wanks. For example, in Vol. 16 No. 9 it will certainly be the double page spread of Pet.

I now have this longing to appear nude in your magazine, and I know that if this happens I would have at least a few youths wanking themselves silly over my picture.

Happy wanking!

Jane, Shropshire

Strictly Vegetarian

I have only recently taken Fiesta regularly (since Vol. 16 No. 6), and I have read your magazine and letters with increasing interest. Having just read Jane of Shropshire's letter (Vol. 17 No. 2) I just had to write to you for the first time.

Jane says she's astonished to learn of the pleasure that some youths get from wanking over girlie mags. Well, I'm one such youth, and I'm nineteen. Jane says that she can confidently tell which pictures in Fiesta will get the most wanks — and here are some of my favourites: in Vol. 17 No.1 both the centrefold picture and the pictures of Ugga had me coming in buckets; and of course there are those wonderful Readers' Wives — Sue (Vol. 16 No. 10), Mary (Vol. 17 No. 4) and Tina (Vol. 17 No. 6).

I'm quite happy giving myself the old right-handed

relief, but I've come up with a few other ideas as well. One of them involves a whole cucumber. I cut one end off, slice it down the middle lengthways, take out the centre together with the seeds and then bind the two halves back together. I then insert the cucumber between the mattress and the bed, kneel down and put my penis inside and push backwards and forwards with my hips until the tight, pleasure-giving grip afforded by the cucumber causes me to come.

I would be very pleased if you could publish my letter for Jane's pleasure — and for that of many other women, wives and girlfriends alike, who are interested in the masturbatory activities of young men.

A.B.S., Staffs.

Slot Metered

I never thought that Fiesta would stimulate more than the wild fantasies I get from looking at the models and (especially) the Readers' Wives, all of whom form the month's supply of tossing off material. While wanking I usually mumble away to the girls' pictures and tell them what they are missing by not being at this address, but the most sexy suggestions come out in really dirty talk with wives at the end of the magazine. This is because they are clearly less bored with having their cunts and tits photographed and seem to be enjoying the fun of sex so much more if their 'come on' expressions are anything to go by. Those expressions often get come on in a rather different way — by my spunk, which jets on to the pages at the moment I imagine myself fucking them and wishing I knew how to be doing it for real.

Special among recent Wives was Karen of Yorkshire (Vol. 16 No. 11) not only because of that very randy look she produces in the first picture, but through a beautiful pair of dugs and that truly astonishing slit that has, as I've said above, stimulated something rather different from the regular and massive erection. Men boast about the size of their pricks and women fantasize about gigantic spunk-spurters, but it was not until I had studied Karen's hole that my astonishment and interest in cunt measurements arose.

The actual length from high up in her pubes to its end, well back in her crotch, must be all of the 10″ that I imagine she was thinking about at the time. If the length of a prick-cosy bears any relationship to its capacity I would reckon she could accommodate anything and anybody and still have room to spare. It certainly exceeds anything I have ever come across — or in. Of course, I would dearly love to see it in its hairy, fleshy and moist magnificence, but all I am able to do is to return to her picture and continue to marvel and fantasize. This I have done on many occasions, and she is by my side as I write.

When I've finished I shall, as usual, deflate the very hard cock I now have in the best way I know how and I shall again have to de-spunk her ready for the next time. I hope Karen will be flattered if I reveal that since last November when she first came into my life I have used her exclusively for wanking and have shot my load looking at her incredible cunt on 43 occasions.

Ted, S.E. London

Reflects Action

I am very interested in letters from readers who take pleasure in wearing their wives' underwear. Whenever my wife goes out for the evening, I go upstairs to our bedroom, close the curtains and start my private act.

Firstly I arrange the mirrors to get the best view of my performance, then I do a striptease show in front of them, which brings on a huge erection. Selecting the most sexy pair of undies from my wife's collection, I pull them up over my crotch and try to contain my prick and balls inside them. This is usually quite difficult, as my balls keep popping out of the sides, and my prick bursts out of the top. Quite a thrilling sensation.

I get so excited by the reflections of myself in the mirrors in this state of sexual ecstasy, that my penis gets very moist and starts dribbling. When I can stand the suspense no longer, I wank myself off and close the show.

Dave, Durham

Look, No Hands

After seven years of reading Fiesta, this is the first time I have ever written in. The reason for doing so is Yvonne of Lancs in Vol. 16 No. 11. The sight of those gorgeous tits protruding through her open bra gave me an immediate urge to stroke my cock to erection. Her beauty made my imagination run wild. I could picture her before me dressed in a leather mini-dress and revealing her stocking-tops. Her gaze would tell me to kneel before her and perform my party trick in her presence to amuse her. In obedience I would gladly perform.

Completely naked, I would admire Yvonne's features and wonderful beauty, getting an erection easily whilst doing so. Not being allowed to touch my cock at all, I have to imagine myself being rubbed by Yvonne's silky fingers. I have to work myself up to a state of excitement at the sight of Yvonne, but still not touching my cock.

By sheer willpower and thought I have to force myself to come — just a little — onto the floor. Being at the complete mercy of Yvonne, I would obey her command to lick up the mess on the floor. Having done so I would then have to finish shooting off the rest of my sperm in front of her. All this would have to be done without touching my cock at all, just by concentrating on the task of coming.

I must confess this fantasy about Yvonne has enabled me to look at her photos in Fiesta and perfect the technique of coming by absolute concentration. I suggest a few other DIY enthusiasts try it. They may find it difficult at first, but with practice the ultimate relief can be achieved with a great feeling of ecstatic release.

Colin, Peterborough

Finger Pickin' Blues

I have tried various ways of wanking whilst looking at the pin-ups in Fiesta, but it is very difficult to hold the page open with one hand, since one needs a third hand with a tissue to catch the sperm — otherwise it shoots all over the pages with sticky consequences.

I have tried using a French letter, but find that this comes off due to fast hand action. The conventional French letter does not give the right sensation with hand massage and is much more suitable when thrusting up some hot damp pussy.

I have tried placing Fiesta on a music stand, thus leaving both hands free, but the snag is that the music room is by the main road and top deck passengers in buses can see right down into the room. I do feel a bit of a prick standing by the music stand, trousers around my ankles and prick out, I suppose I could make out that I'm merely studying Bach's Organ Prelude.

How about having a Fiesta centre page pull-out with a hole cut through the cunt, with a french letter fixed behind on a sponge cushion. This could then be pinned to a mattress and given a right going over.

Maybe other readers have some suggestions, since though there is nothing like a dame, in the absence of a willing and available female it's back to the old five fingers.

Horny, Hampstead

Swimmers' Strokes

I would like to relate a sexy little episode to you. I'm afraid it may seem a little tame by the standards of some of your readers, but it did actually take place.

I was on holiday with my wife, her sister Mary and Mary's husband in a four berth chalet in Clacton. On this particular day we had all been swimming, but my wife decided she needed to get some shopping. Mary's husband volunteered to take her down to the shops, as we only had one car, which was his. Mary and I returned to the chalet to dry off and change.

Mary never fails to excite me. She is thirty years old and quite tall, and has small jutting tits and an ample bum. The mound of her fanny, her tits and her arse were all straining on the wet material of her swimsuit. Although I was not fully erect, my heart was beating fast in my throat by the time we reached the chalet, and I went straight to my room, pulled down my trunks and started to pull away at my throbbing cock. The thought of Mary stripping off her flimsy costume was making my head spin.

Suddenly the door burst open, and there was Mary staring at me, mouth agape. She muttered that she thought I was in the toilet and that she had come into my room to borrow my wife's dressing gown.

I said, 'I'm sorry Mary, but I just can't help it!' She laughed nervously and said she was surprised her body would get me excited at all. In this situation I thought I now might as well chance my arm. 'You're at an advantage,' I said. 'You've seen me, now how about I get a look at you, to give me something to really wank about.'

She hesitated at first, then pulled down the top of her costume, revealing her small jutting tits, and carried on pulling it down to expose a veritable undergrowth of black public hair. I spunked immediately but carried on wanking. Mary watched avidly, moving around on the spot and squeezing her ample thighs together. 'Oh, for fuck's sake, wank me,' I cried.

She came over, pulled my foreskin back and wanked me

as though I was circumcised, as apparently is her husband. She told me she wanted to fuck, but couldn't live with it — me being her sister's husband. However, she told me to lie down, then she straddled across me and held the tip of my cock just barely muzzling into her slit. Then, at amazing speed, she started to wank us both at the same time, using my cock like a dildo.

After a couple of minutes of this I spunked again, over her slit. She lay back and wanked herself, using my spunk as lubrication, until she came — almost like a bloke as her thick come blobbed out.

Surprisingly, it was not embarrassing afterwards, and we have these joint wanking sessions whenever possible now. Her peculiar code of ethics and conduct will still not allow her to be fucked by me — but I'm working on it.

Spencer, Romford

It Takes One To Tango
I would be interested to learn if there are any of your readers who share my particular pastime — wanking off to music.

Over the years I have tossed myself off to many fine tunes including *Rule Britannia, Land of Hope and Glory, 76 Trombones,* and when I'm in the mood for the classics I listen to the *Nutcracker Suite* (which is particularly good for a slow toss) or the *Flight of the Bumble Bee* (for a more energetic time).

I use my cock in the same way as a conductor uses his baton — waving it around in time to the music and beating up and down in time to the rhythm.

I hope this will be of interest to those of your readers with a musical 'bent'.

Ian, Sussex

Getting It Taped

I've read many times in magazines about people seeing couples having sex. Well, just before Christmas I visited a video club where they show porno movies, and I arrived, as usual, with a pair of navy blue knickers to wank in if I had the chance.

It was very quiet, with only three people in the thirty seat club. I sat at the back, and about two minutes after I had taken my seat a man and a woman came and sat in seats in the row in front of me, just to the left.

The woman sat nearest me, with her legs crossed. The man put his hand on her knee and pushed her skirt up a bit. I watched the film for a while with my prick enclosed in the navy knickers. Then I saw a movement out of the corner of my eye, and noticed the woman was moving around in her seat, leaning slightly forward. Turning my attention from the screen, I was just in time to notice her removing her light coloured panties.

For a while there was not much movement in front of me, then I saw a distinct movement of her right arm. She was giving her companion a wank. He turned slightly and whispered in her ear, whereupon her head bobbed down onto his lap.

I lost interest in the film completely as I realised that she was sucking his cock. The man reached down her back and worked his hand between her legs and I had a nice view of a plump bum with a hand fingering her cunt as I leaned forward for a better look.

Whether the man came or not I don't know, but I did, right into the knickers. A few more whispers and the girl got up and I saw the man's prick standing up. She tried to sit on his lap and even with the two of them trying to achieve their goal, it was clear they were not going to succeed. All the time the girl seemed to be looking at me. They gave up after a few minutes and she went down on his cock again. This time I'm sure he came, and as he did I shot my second load into the navy knickers.

Peace and quiet ruled for a while, and then I noticed

194

that the woman's legs were well spread. Another upheaval in front of me and the man was on the floor. It must have been uncomfortable, but he managed to get there and started sucking her cunt. My hand was wanking like mad when the girl grabbed the man's head, groaned, turned and looked straight at me as I deposited some more spunk in the knickers.

I had to leave then, before I wanked myself silly. I'm going there again tomorrow night, in the hope they will be there to give me another private show.

Bob, Devon

Homes And Gardeners

My husband Mike and I have been taking your magazine for a year now and we love to read the letters. We have been married for three years and we are both 29.

Mike and I have always been interested in the letters concerning masturbation. Unfortunately Mike trucks a good deal during the week and is sometimes away from home Monday to Friday. During these periods apart, I spend my evenings wanking. Mike has fixed me up with a good collection of vibrators, dildos and other sex toys and on some occasions I can bring myself off three or four times in an evening before going to bed. When Mike gets home at weekends I tell him about my wanking sessions and he really gets turned on. He loves to watch me fingering my cunt or using one of the dildos. Then we have a lovely fuck while I tell him what I have been fantasising about during the week.

One of my favourite fantasies is to be caught wanking by our gardener who attends to our garden twice a week. He is a young lad of 18, but for some reason it gets me going to think about him watching me as I wank myself. Mike knows about this fantasy and has often suggested that I would do no harm to let him watch.

Mike knows him better than I do, and one evening a

month or so ago Mike invited him round for a drink. We all got very pissed and Mike put some porno movies on the video (something else that turns me on when I am wanking on my own). The atmosphere was electric after about ten minutes of this and Dave, our guest, was rubbing his prick through his jeans.

Mike and I were sat on the sofa opposite, and Mike took his prick out and started to wank himself. I undid my blouse to expose my tits and pulled up my skirt. I had no knickers on, and I started to rub my fanny. Dave looked round when he saw what I was up to. He took out his own cock and started to wank in full view of Mike and I. Seconds later I had my first come of the evening.

Mike then lay me down on the carpet and thrust his cock deep inside me. I could see Dave watching intently. I called out to him to come nearer so he could kiss me. Soon Dave and I were french kissing while Mike took Dave's hand and placed it on my right tit. I reached out and took hold of Dave's prick and wanked it for him. Almost immediately I felt his spunk shooting through my fingers onto the carpet. Mike could hold back no longer and shot his load into my cunt.

Since the first encounter, Dave has returned several times for similar sessions.

Judith & Mike, Lancs.

A Warm Hand . . .
Having been a Fiesta reader for quite a few years now, I hope you don't mind if I write to thank you. I am a dedicated wanker and have yet to find another mag that provides me with so many fantastic spunk-ups.

This may be a new one for your records, but my almost total hang-up is sex words. Reading your stories, articles and especially the letters full of words like cunt, prick, spunk, shag, fuck and particularly wank can raise my cock to its 7″ limit (why exaggerate?) and set my balls churning the spunk around. The pictures of fuckable females with suckable cunts set my blood racing, but the captions, if spicy enough, will set my spunk spurting.

I am well aware that some of you at Fiesta will say 'Get yourself a woman and stop being a retarded wanker.' (*Not at all — Ed.*). The fact is, I do have women, but even after a good fuck I still enjoy an old-fashioned wank.

I don't need a head-shrinker to tell me how I became latched on to dirty words and a compulsive tosser. When I was about thirteen I accidentally found a sex magazine. I almost passed out when my eyes caught those words in print for the first time. 'He fucked her steadily, her cunt tight and juicy, his hard, long prick shafting in and out, his large hairy balls almost bursting to release the boiling spunk.'

Although I had, on occasions, played with my fast developing cock, that night I had a mind-blowing, fully fledged wank and shot my first ever load of come. Since then I have been a dirty word fanatic and connected them with a good wank and fantastic spunking.

I'm sure I have said enough, but I would just like to make a couple of suggestions. One: give us wankers at least a page each issue for letters and stories devoted to our favourite hobby — you could call it DIY Corner or Fiesta Wankers Club. Two: print a really good article on the subject of wanking. If you had some small badges or even car-stickers with 'I belong to the F.W.C.' printed, I would be the first customer.

D.G., Yorks.

. . . And Sticky Fingers

I was very interested in the letter from Jane of Shropshire in Vol. 17 No. 1, concerning her interest in the masturbatory activities of 'young male virgins.' As an 18-year-old male myself, I hope she, and you, will find my views on the subject interesting.

I should start by saying that I began wanking about five years ago, and I have not looked back since. I keep a supply of girlie mags (Fiesta, of course) which I like to wank over. I have to be careful, though, as I live with my parents, but I usually manage one session a day, often more.

My best wanking sessions take place when my parents are out for the evening, and I have several hours to myself. I then go to my bedroom and start to strip off. By the time I get down to my underpants, I always have a massive hard-on in anticipation of the pleasure to come. I slip my underpants off and get out my selection of mags. I then slowly wank myself whilst reading, especially the readers' letters, and admiring the bodies of the beautiful girls. I particularly like big-chested girls, and as I wank I like to imagine my prick being massaged by a lovely pair of tits. I usually do this for anything up to two hours, until I feel I can wait no longer and have to relieve the pressure. I then turn to the girl who has most turned me on and concentrate on her, whilst steadily increasing the pace of my right hand.

After such a long wait, the orgasm is always fantastic. The feelings of ecstasy emanating from my groin build up to a great height, until my balls finally erupt, shooting their load in long spurts over my chest and face and spattering the mag. The sheer ecstasy as I come is in indescribable, and I get a great thrill from seeing my throbbing prick shooting long spurts of hot spunk.

As you can tell, I really enjoy my frequent masturbation sessions, and I am not ashamed to admit to being a devoted wanker. I would just like to finish by thanking Jane for writing the original letter and sending in the pictures of herself. The one of you wearing those black stockings and suspenders with the panties telling me to 'wank now' really turned me on, and I've had several great wanks over it, although it's now rather stained due to the amount of spunk I've shot over it. I hope you don't mind!

Phil, Middlesex

Called To The Bra

My wife is absent seeing her family in Australia, and so for the last few months I have been rediscovering the techniques of masturbation. I remember in younger years often trying out different means of achieving orgasm, other than by the normal 'left hander'.

One way that I have perfected is to use a bra. I like the idea of finding alternative uses for such items. I am rather delighted with the technique I have developed, and I thought I would write to share the secret with other Fiesta readers, and also to perhaps prompt others to interchange their own ideas for non-manual wanking.

First one has to obtain a suitable bra. I discovered mine by trial and error. Ideally it wants to be low cut, stretchy and with wide straps which are also stretchy. I have found the cross-your-heart variety quite handy.

I fasten the garment round my legs — clasp at the rear, cups to the front and with the shoulder straps laying downwards on my thighs. I then pull on a pair of stretch nylon pants over my erection — the more stretching the better, but they should be fairly tight. With my erect cock jutting forward in the panties I then loop the bra straps over my cock and adjust the position of the bra so that pleasant feelings are obtained by thrusting my bum forward and back, in the fashion of intercourse.

The prick is held firm by the bra straps, and the motion of my hips draw the skin backwards and forwards in the necessary fashion. The firm resistance of the stretch panties gives a pleasant stimulation of the glans in the manner of thrusting into the cervix of a woman. Sometimes I adjust things so that, for example, the same effect can be achieved by laying on the ground and raising and lowering my legs in turn.

I find this a pleasant diversion during my wife's absence, as I prefer not to date any other girl. I also buy my own requirements as I would not want to break faith with my wife.

George, Cambs.

Strange Bedfellows

Knowing the keen interest you and your readers have in the more unexpected aspects of sex, and guessing that more than a few of them might not be averse to an occasional bit of wanking, you may be interested in a recent experience of mine which concerned both.

I've, done quite a bit of sexy photography in my time, and recently at a club I got friendly with a chap in his late 40s. To cut it short, he invited me home one day to see his photos. I arrived all keen, and was a bit surprised to meet his wife there too — in her late 40s I guessed, slim and shapely, but not really attractive to look at. All very pleasant, sat having coffee, friend went to get photos, arrived with a couple of boxes, opened one, thrust a handful at me. These were nice, model-sessions, typical of the amateur model set-up. The next lot were riper, with some 'continental poses' by one girl. I was a tiny bit embarrassed, as wifey was still with us, joining in the chat. The crunch was the next lot he gave me. I looked down and couldn't believe my eyes, as there were he and wifey, stark naked, and having it off in a wide variety of ways, with lots of cock-sucking close-ups, and plenty of remarkably detailed photos of the family fanny. I didn't know what to do, but said a few things like, 'Yes, very nice' and 'I like that one'. This went on for some time, and I got used to the idea. Wifey was unmoved — not embarrassed, but not in the least turned on by it.

Suddenly, my friend blurted out 'Do you usually wank over photos in Fiesta and so on? I know I do, every month, don't I darling?' She nodded, and I nearly fell off the settee with horror. I mumbled something about 'it all depends really' and he then went on about the photos, and tossing off, as one of the combinations he liked best in sex. I began to relax, and frankly to feel a bit sexy, looking at cunt photos of his wife whilst she sat opposite, with him discussing sex with her and me.

At this point, he passed me another set, which was of her alone, stripping off and then wanking herself with her fingers, and then a few other things from the kitchen, and finally sitting over what I guessed was his cock. I whistled, and he said 'Makes you randy doesn't it, eh?' I nodded. He followed up by bluntly saying, 'I fancy a wank now, would you mind?'. I didn't really know what to do, but I said, 'Well no of course not', upon which he unzipped, fumbled around, produced a stiff prick, and proceeded to wank away cheerfully. I glanced at wifey, who was still looking at the photos: she looked up, and said, 'Oh don't mind me, I've seen it all before, so carry on. . .' I decided to be stupid, unzipped, and produced the pride and joy. It was him, not her (unfortunately) who said, 'Wheh, that's nice. Do you wank often?' I felt a bit ridiculous, sitting on the settee, wanking along beside him, while his wife largely ignored us. So I said, 'Yes, quite a bit, but usually in private.' He then said, 'Have you tried the old settee or bed trick?' I gulped and wondered what the hell next, but said, 'No, what is it?'

He said, 'Come upstairs if you like, and I'll show you'. I was a bit nervous, but pretty randy, so up I went, prick dangling. He got into their bedroom, whipped off his trousers and pants, knelt down, and gently inserted his prick between the mattress and the divan, and started slowly thrusting. I decided to join him, and did the same — and I must admit it was very nice. He said, 'Of course it's better with a silk lining', got up, and produced two pairs of silky panties from a drawer, gave one to me, and used this to provide a silken lining to the imitation cunt. I did the same, and frankly it was bloody good, thrusting in and out.

At this moment, wifey could be heard mounting the stairs, and said from outside, 'Can I come in?' Before I could say anything, he said, 'Yes,' and in she tripped, bringing, would you believe it, two cups of tea. 'Thought you would like these,' she said, ignoring the fact that her husband and an unknown male were fucking her bed. She glanced at us for a while, came behind him and rubbed her skirt on the back of his head, looked at me, and then did the same to me. As she stood there, I started to come, and frantically fucked away as she rubbed her thighs on my head and he yelled, 'Go on, go on, great isn't it?' I came in an explosion. She bent down and pulled friend's prick out from the bed and proceeded to toss him off — in fact he must have been almost there as he came all over her hand at once. She then disappeared and I didn't see her again.

Friend then became entirely matter-of-fact, we went downstairs, arranged to meet at the next photo club session, and I said, 'Thanks very much,' and he said, 'That's okay I enjoy a good wank,' and that was that.

OK, so don't believe it, but it DID happen, and a silky bed-fuck is bloody good, so try it yourself!

Jim, Hants.

Handy With Mandy

I am now 40 and have been married for 21 years to a woman I love very much, but alas she has become very frigid in recent years. To compensate for this I wank quite regularly, and use the wonderful Readers' Wives section of Fiesta to stimulate my imagination. By doing this I can fantasise a fuck whenever I please.

There is one woman who never fails to bring my prick to attention, and she is Mandy, Yorks in Vol. 16 No. 7. I don't know whether it is her lovely full tits, or her equally lovely thick hairy fanny that turns me on — or maybe it's just that look in her eyes that says, 'Come and fuck me!' Anyway, I have imagined that I have fucked this lady many, many times. Let me tell you how I go about it.

First of all I lay starkers on the bed, with my prick in hand and your magazine propped up against the bedside lamp. I look at Mandy in her black stockings and suspenders, and I start wanking slowly. Very soon my imagiation starts working, and she is lying beside me. I am sucking her tits and giving her two full fingers right up her gorgeous hairy fanny, while she is wanking my prick with her experienced fingers. She is pushing my foreskin back as far as possible and exposing my swollen bell-end, which she in turn kisses, licks, and finally takes in her beautiful mouth. (Now my imagination is really working overtime, and so is my wanking hand.)

As she takes my prick from her mouth she moves up the bed beside me, pulls my prick over to her open cunt, but just allows the head of it to rub inside her juicy wet lips. I am eager to enter her slit, but she puts her hand round my balls and, with a squeeze, stops me from entering her.

I am now going crazy, and ready for bursting when Mandy puts her beautiful legs astride my body and mounts me, taking hold of my thick stiff prick and guiding it into her now dripping fanny. Slowly she starts to ride me, savouring the length and thickness of my weapon. As her stroke quickens her lovely big tits bounce up and down in rhythm with her well rounded arse.

Soon we are in a frenzy of love and lust as she sits back on my throbbing prick, taking the full 8½″ deep inside her demanding cunt. Just at that moment I look at Mandy's photo and visualise the both of us going from one shattering climax to another.

Then it is back to reality and my spunk is shooting all over the place. I have had Mandy and many other Readers' Wives in this fantasy world of mine, and it gets better every time — especially with Mandy. I would love to fuck her for real — but then sometimes I believe that I have! She is the best fuck in my world.

Mick, London

Solo Sessions

What a turn-on it was to read the letter in Vol 15 No 4 in which F.P. of London describes his fun and games. I'm sure he would like to know that there are others who also like a little something extra on the side without going astray.

Like him, I am blessed with a good sex-life at home — nothing too kinky, but plenty of variety. Yet I seem as though I must have a bit of solo when I'm feeling randy and have the house to myself, though I don't have the luxury of a remote-controlled Polaroid to record my activities.

But I can enjoy myself in my own little way with my vivid fantasies. I can withold my ejaculation for almost an hour and a half — until I simply have to let fly. I must agree, the come off is mind-blowing.

I had tried his method of masturbating, with one hand tickling balls and anus — but not the wet finger up and down below the glans. I simply had to try it. It was great.

T.P., Nottingham

7. TV TIMES

Wham, Bam,
   Thank You Pam
Blushy Peas?
WCTV
New Pleasures
Fifties' Fashions

TV Or Not TV?
TV Sisters
Frilling Games
Transexual's Plea
TV Bargain

Wham, Bam, Thank You Pam

I am sending you a photo of my husband, who I call Pamela, as I thought your readers might like to see him as he really is.

I've bought him a complete wardrobe of the sexiest clothes I could find and I make him wear them all the time. I quite often have friends round for coffee and he is more than pleased to act as maid. Quite often his cock is exposed for these occasions, but I thought this might be a bit much for your magazine. I very nearly let him fuck me, but first I make him lick my juicy cunt for a very long time. When I'm in the mood I will make him suck my strap-on dildo, and the sight of him trying to suck my 14″ prick will be enough to bring me to orgasm.

I know that both my husband and my friends will be thrilled to see his picture and this letter in your magazine.

You may be intersted to know that whilst writing this letter, Pamela is between my stockinged legs, tickling my fanny through my open crotch panties, and his hands are on my nipples.

Patricia, Clwyd

Blushy Peas?

I am a married man, aged 30, and I have found that my biggest turn-on is to be embarrassed in front of women. As I can't tell my wife about it, I have devised 3 ways to achieve this.

1 I wear a see-through shirt with a dark bra underneath and a jacket on top. When I pass by a group of girls I undo

my jacket and nearly always one will notice and tell her mates. They then look and nearly always laugh at me or shout out something.

2 I will wear suspenders and stockings with a pair of frilly undies. I then go in a clothes boutique with curtains across the changing room. I will try on a few pairs of trousers, making sure there is a gap in my curtain. My biggest moment came when a lady pushing a push chair walked by and the baby pulled open my curtain, showing me to a group of girls and staff of the shop.

3 I will wet myself and walk through a park. Out of them all, this one is least noticed.

Do any of your readers have my kink, as I have been reading your mag for months but have not read about anyone else who gets their kicks like I do.

J.B., Wiltshire

WCTV

I would like to reply to a letter you had in an earlier Fiesta about transvestites and how they go to the toilet while out dressed as a woman.

First a little about me. I am happily married with a wife who knows about — and even helps me with — my need to cross dress. She helps by buying clothes and make up with us both in mind, and she has shown me how to put on make up. Even now, while I sit here alone writing this letter, I am dressed as a woman. I have on a pink bra and knickers, black lace underskirt with white frills, stockings, tan sandals and a black pencil skirt and a see-through blouse and jumper. To top this off, I have got a long curled wig which is the same shade as my own hair, which makes it look real.

Now for what happened to me some weeks ago. As my garage is connected to the house, I can leave home dressed as I please. One day I got dressed as a woman, make up and all, put a few things into one of my handbags and with my lady's coat over my arm I left the house by the garage door and drove off heading towards the coast.

Some 30 minutes later I felt the need to visit the toilet. Well, as there was snow on the ground I decided not to go behind a bush, but drove on trying to find a public toilet. Eventually, I came across a road sign saying there was a toilet half a mile up the road so at great speed I headed for it.

When I arrived, to my horror, I found it was in a pub. The sign said it was around the side, and as it looked empty I took the chance — only to discover it was behind the bar. I was having second thoughts as to whether to go in or not, when two men got out of a car and headed my way. I went in, only to find that the cubicle was locked so I had to wait for what seemed like hours but was only minutes. The girl came out of the cubicle and went over to the sinks so I jumped into the cubicle, locked it and sat down to have my wee.

As I left, the girl was waiting for me by the door. She stopped me and asked me straight out if I was a man. What could I say but 'Yes love, I am'. She was very calm about it all, while I was like a cat on a hot tin roof. She saw I was in a bad way and said, 'Let's get out of here before anyone else comes in'. As we went through the bar she called to a girl friend to meet us out front — but when her friend joined up with us outside I could have died for it was not a girl, but a fellow T.V. out for a drink with his wife. I made arrangements to meet them the following week with my wife, providing she would come out with me while dressed up.

To my delight, she agreed and came out with me that week, and all four of us meet every week for a chat or a drink.

V., Colchester

New Pleasures

I find it very interesting that so many of your male readers are so turned on by women's underwear. My husband, Adrian, and I have been married for eight years and have enjoyed a reasonable sex life. However, until quite recently, I had not discovered Adrian's fetish for wearing my underwear.

Every Thursday night I go to my squash club, while Adrian stays in and looks after our baby daughter. However, this particular night my opponent left a message at the club to say she couldn't make it, so I decided to return home.

Creeping into the house so as not to wake the baby, I found no sign of Adrian. So I went upstairs, and looking through the crack in the door, I saw him. . .

He was lying on the bed with a sex magazine — and wearing a pair of sheer black stockings, white suspender-belt and a pair of my white frilly knickers. His erect penis was sticking out of the top of the knickers and he was slowly caressing it with his free hand.

Well, as you can imagine, I was absolutely startled. My first reaction was anger, but then I began to wonder if I had been insensitive to his sexual needs. The more I thought about it, the randier I got as I watched Adrian slowly masturbating. I decided without further ado to walk in on him. He was obviously taken by surprise and didn't know what to say, but I soon put him at his ease.

'So you want to be turned on, do you?' I said, starting to remove my clothes until all that remained was a pair of French knickers.

Adrian was breathing heavily and was obviously getting excited as I straddled him on the bed in the 69 position and took his huge penis in my mouth. As I sucked him I gently caressed the top of his legs which were encased in my sheer nylon stockings, while he rubbed his face and hands over my silky knickers.

By this stage he was going absolutely wild. I could feel his tool throbbing strongly in my mouth, but I tantalised him by refusing to let him come. Every time he was close to shooting his load. I would remove his prick from my mouth and just lightly tickle the shiny head with my tongue. At the same time my hands were inside his knickers caressing his balls. As he desperately tried to force his prick further into my mouth, he was begging me to make him come.

After about fifteen minutes of this torture, I finally took his whole prick deep in my mouth, and in no more than two or three strokes his warm come was pumping into my mouth. I never realised he had so much come in him.

We then lay together on the bed for over an hour, by which time Adrian's prick began to stir again, thankfully, as I still hadn't been satisfied. I didn't even remove my knickers, I simply moved the gusset to one side as he thrust his prick into me. Because he had already come, his staying power was great and it was my turn to be tortured by him not allowing me to come. He kept on pumping me for more than half an hour, until we both reached a climax together — something we had found difficult to achieve before.

It had been many years since Adrian and I had enjoyed such a passionate night. However, I don't let him wear my underwear all the time because I don't want the novelty of it to wear off. But I'm pleased that he doesn't have to wear my underwear and masturbate in secret anymore.

I would therefore urge any wives or girlfriends who believe their men have a similar fetish to encourage it and bring it out into the open and their own sex life will improve, as mine has.

Elaine, Staffs.

Fifties' Fashions
My turn-on is ladies' underwear of the '50s and '60s. Oh, those lovely shiny high-waisted girdles with adjustable suspenders, fully fashioned seamed nylons and clingy satin

knickers! Many is the time I've gone out stocking-top viewing in pubs, or in the parks in summertime. To catch sight of dark stocking-tops, straining suspenders, white thigh and knicker legs with taut gusset gives me a tremendous throbbing hard-on. And the thrill is even greater if the lady in question knows that I know that she knows I'm watching.

In the end I started wearing ladies' undies myself — girdles, seamed stockings and shiny knickers. It's a gorgeous sight to stand in front of a mirror dressed like this, with my suspenders done up tight, my knickers around my knees, and my cock heavy over my balls.

I usually have a mag like Fiesta in front of me, with your suspender-clad girls on display. My prick visibly lifts and becomes erect, my knob-end becoming a deep red in colour.

I have a long slow toss and let my come shoot out in front of me, or pull my knickers up and soak them with passion juice. Or I push my cock up flat against my stomach with my corset pulled down over it. A few movements back and forth and the spunk really floods out and eventually runs down over my balls.

The ideal situation for me is to get all my undies on and then have a woman dress up the same. Then she walks round the room, posing for me in different positions while I toss my cock off through my knickers.

Finally, I get her to bend over a chair while I stuff her from behind with my iron-hard prick up her knicker-leg and deep into her cunt. I then give her a good hard fuck while I hang onto her tits, and I love to see my spunk running down over her stocking-tops.

Alan, Tyneside

TV Or Not TV?

I would like to contribute to your readers' enjoyment of the letters in Fiesta by telling you of an experience I shared with my fiancee, Lorraine, a couple of weeks ago.

Lorraine has always been a highly sexed girl, and on the occasion I am writing about she was sitting in our living room reading my Fiestas whilst I was out doing some shopping. When I returned from the trip to the shops, I looked into the living room as I hung my coat up and saw that she was still reading, but it was obvious that one hand was up her skirt. From the movements she was making I realised she had settled down to a good wanking session. As she had not noticed me return, I decided to watch her quietly.

She hitched up her skirt well above her stocking tops and I could see the hairy fringes of her lovely pussy peeping out from behind her knicks. Her fingers began to stroke her clitoris through the fabric and as her fingers moved faster she began to moan softly and squirm about as her orgasm approached. By this time I had a huge hard on, and I decided to slip into the bedroom and give her a surprise. I stripped off and put on one of her suspender belts, rolling a pair of dark tan stockings onto my legs. Then I selected a pair of wide-legged satin French knickers and got into them. The feeling of taut nylon against my skin was almost too much for me, I hadn't been so hard for ages. Thus attired I returned to my hiding place, just outside the sitting room, and resumed watching the show.

Lorraine was on the verge of coming. She was playing with her clit and three fingers of her other hand were frigging her obviously soaking wet cunt. I could hear her whispering obscenities between her moans. I decided that this was the time to make my entrance.

When she saw me in her underwear her eyes nearly popped out of their sockets. This seemed to be all she needed, for she came to a noisy orgasm immediately, shouting out: 'Fuck me for Heaven's sake.' I walked over to her and she dropped to her knees, taking my knob in her mouth, rubbing her hands up and down my nylon clad legs. I pulled my cock out of her mouth, lay on the floor and told her to fuck me.

'Oh yes,' she replied, lowering herself onto my throbbing cock, 'I want this prick right up my cunt and I want to be filled with your spunk, you bastard.' She started moving up and down on my cock, moaning, 'Fuck, fuck, fuck,' over and over again. Her juices ran down and soaked my pubic hair as she moved faster and faster. Then she moved off me, knelt on the floor, presenting the cheeks of her arse to me, and demanded that I fuck her cunt from behind.

I got up and shafted her lovely tight cunt from behind, as she cried out, 'I'm coming, fuck me harder.' The feeling of our nylon clad legs rubbing together and her buttocks banging against my satin covered hips was wonderful. I thrust my full length into her as she came even more noisily than before. As she came she reached her hand back and gently squeezed my balls. This proved too much for me and I shot my come deep into her quim.

We both lay on the floor, exhausted but very satisfied. Later Lorraine confessed that she had always wanted me to wear her undies but had never dared ask me. Now she is talking about me taking some photos of her for the Readers' Wives Section, so who knows?

Jack, London

TV Sisters

May I congratulate you on your magazine, of which I have been a regular reader for some three years. I particularly like the way you cover a wide range of aspects of sexual behaviour, with something to please most tastes. I myself have only recently discovered what my particular fetish is and would like to explain my discovery for the interest of your readers.

I am a 26 year old single male and I consider myself to be quite broad-minded where sex is concerned. I have had many girlfriends and have had intercourse with a large number of females. However, last Saturday evening I was round at Jane's place, (my latest girlfriend), having just taken her to see the film *Tootsie*. We discussed it and I said it was rubbish. Jane said she thought it was terrific, especially the way Dustin Hoffman played the part of the woman so convincingly.

At this point, I said it wasn't so special, that anyone could do it. 'Oh yeah?' said Jane, 'let's see you do it.' I didn't take her up on it, but she persisted. 'Come on, smarty, let's see how good you are in the garb.' She disappeared into her bedroom and re-emerged carrying some articles of clothing. Placing these on the sofa beside me, she told me to strip off, which I did, and she led me to the bathroom.

Once there, she proceeded to shave all the hair off my legs and, satisfied that she had missed nothing, she led me back into the living room and handed me a pair of blue nylon panties. This was followed by dark brown tights, black lacy bra (padded out) and a long-length, black nylon petticoat.

By this time, I had an enormous erection which Jane was not slow in noticing. 'Hey,' she said, touching me gently, 'I do believe this is turning you on.' She then handed me a dress to put on, which fell just below my knees, and finally I squeezed my feet into a pair of her low-heeled shoes. 'I think some make-up would do nicely,' she said, admiring my figure and starting to work on my face.

When she had finished the artwork, she guided me through to her bedroom (I was still a little unsteady) where the full-length wall mirror was situated. The reflection that caught my eye sent shivers down my spine. Staring back at me was quite a passable feminine figure. I was amazed at the transformation. Seeing myself in female garments really aroused me and, lifting my dress plus petticoat, I looked hard at my legs cased in nylons, then at the pretty panties that enclosed my cock and balls.

Jane completed the picture by handing me one of her handbags, combing my hair into a feminine style and saying, 'Let's go shopping.' I refused point blank, saying that I couldn't possibly pass for a female. 'Like hell you couldn't,' replied Jane, 'not even your best friend would recognise you.' I chanced it. For the next three hours, Jane and I wandered around shops like two sisters and I'm certain no one saw through my disguise.

When we returned home, I actually felt like a female and quite at home in feminine undies, etc. When Jane told me I had better get changed, I felt very disappointed. Jane noticed it immediately because she asked me how much I enjoyed wearing female underwear. I tried, as best I could, to explain my feelings and Jane, being a very understanding lady, promised me that in future whenever I felt the urge, I could dress up in her clothes.

Before going home that night, Jane and I ended up making love, both of us dressed in very silky, feminine underwear. The experience was mind-blowing. For *both* of us, as Jane explained that she really got a kick out of it also. Now, at least once a week, I dress in Jane's sexy clothes and both of us venture out to different places. I am much more confident now. I know I can pass for quite a pretty girl.

B.C., Hamilton

Frilling Games
I have been interested of late in all the letters from men who bring themselves off while wearing their wives frilly underwear. I love to wear my wife's undies, in fact I buy and choose most of her underwear with myself in mind.

One day I was dressed up in a red frilly lace suspender-belt, black stockings and French see-through knickers, reading a copy of Fiesta, when I heard my wife coming upstairs. Quickly covering myself I pretended to be asleep and watched out of the corner of my eye as my wife stripped to her bra and panties and went to the drawer where she keeps her undies. She looked puzzled as she pulled out her suspender-belt, stockings and open-front panties. Then she came over to the bed and pulled back the sheets to reveal me in her undies. She did not look at all surprised, but gently moved my panties to one side and started tossing me off. By now my cock was just about bursting as she told me that she knew all about me wearing her underwear. She suggested we made love, but first she wanted to suck me off until I came in her mouth — something she had never done before.

As I was to discover later, my wife told her best friend, Ann, all about that exciting morning. This got Ann going so much that she wet her pants and asked my wife if she could see for herself. My wife agreed and planned for me to dress up in her best frilly undies, telling me that she would come back later to suck me off.

Oblivious to her plans, I fell asleep, waking some time later to find my wife licking my balls. I was enjoying this so much that it was some while before I noticed Ann near the bedroom door, clad only in a green garter-belt and stockings. When she walked over to me and asked if she could give me a blow job I just smiled in reply. She bent down and removed my cock from my wife's mouth and slowly sucked it deep into her own. I can tell you it was the best suck I have ever had and it wasn't long before she was swallowing every drop of my spunk.

Now Ann comes round every other Wednesday to dress me up in sexy undies which she buys for herself and me. She loves to give me a tit-wank between her lovely big 38C's so that I can shoot my cum into her mouth. All three of us are very happy fucking, licking and sucking in each other's company.

So here's to frilly undies and cock-sucking wives and last, but not least, randy Ann who has changed our whole sex life. She has tried to get her hubby to wear undies, but he won't, so Ann comes to suck my pantie-covered cock. . .

John, Pam and Ann

Transexual's Plea

I enjoy reading the letters from the many TVs who appear to amuse themselves and get sexual pleasure from female dress and underwear, which is nice for them if that's how they want it.

I'm enclosing a couple of photos of my 'girlfriend' — which you will soon realise is, in fact, myself. I'm not a TV, but a transexual, and the 36B bust is not padding but all me. Like TVs I enjoy wearing sexy underwear, but unlike them I don't get sexually turned on by it, what I get is a sense of satisfaction and fulfilment.

I must point out that I am married, with two kids, heterosexual and a believer in monogamy. My work keeps me away from home for long periods, with usually only one night a week at home. If that coincides with my wife's period or 'headache' or whatever, then not wishing to enter into an extra-marital affair with all its attendant risks I create my own 'girlfriend' in order to have some contact with the opposite sex.

I wear stockings, suspenders and black undewear — which my wife refuses to do. I find tights very inconvenient and sweaty to wear, and I consider them sexless garments and definitely unfeminine. On the wages I get I couldn't afford a girlfriend anyway.

I was transexual for many years prior to marriage, which was undertaken partly to bow to family pressures — though they didn't know about the other me — and partly because I knew I could never afford a sex-change operation on my wages.

I knew that my lower half was normal and functioned as it should, it was just the upper half and my mind that told me that I was different or ought to be. I went through all the classic stages, experimenting, make-up, dressing-up, venturing out in public, etc., and believe me, it's a mind-blowing trauma.

Eventually I came to terms with it all and rarely try to hide it, except from my work colleagues, some of whom do suspect, I think, but don't know for sure and I don't tell them anyway. I avoid them after hours and keep to myself. It's a lonely life as a transexual, but I'm used to it now.

But the main reason for my letter is what I am going to say next, which carries on with a theme aired recently in Fiesta. It's the oft-raised question: why is it still legally an offence for a male to appear in public dressed as a female, when vice-versa it is not even noticed?

I have been doing it for years, with practised attention to detail, and I have got away with it, apart from a few odd slips in early days, which were more embarrassing than anything else.

I have once been stopped by the police in Lincolnshire while out walking alone late one night, just as a routine check. When I explained my circumstances to them they were quite amicable and we mutually agreed that so long as I kept my nose clean and gave them no trouble, then I'd get no trouble from them.

And so it was for five years, until I moved to pastures new. I wish all policemen had the same enlightened adult attitude to people like me and allowed us free movement about the towns and countryside unmolested, only picking on those who really abuse the normal codes of decency. I do believe that transexuals should be accepted in society in a normal decent manner and left alone by the law to live our lives as we feel we want to.

I would be very interested to hear from members of the law if they also believe this, since medical science now recognises transexual people as a fact, then why doesn't the law do so? Whatever happened to equal rights? Equal for whom? Certainly not for transexuals, it would seem.

The photos prove that I can look the part, much the

same as any other girl. People even say I have nice legs —
what do you think? I go shopping during the daytime
dressed up and judging by the whistles and toots I get I
don't seem to be offending the eye of the beholder. It
would be nice to think that some MP may read this and
think that it's about time this legal anomaly was amended
and soon.

Do those who knock people like myself realise that
when I go out at night alone I am subject to the very same
risks that other single girls are subject to, sexual attacks
and muggings which are so prevalent in our sick society? I
for one would run a mile to avoid trouble and I keep a
good look-out.

Most transexuals are very gentle and honest people, so
give us a break, don't ridicule us, accept us for what we
are, neither all male or all female. Let us live as we feel
most comfortable and leave us to live without hindrance.
It's hard enough being like this without society making it
harder.

Very Lonely Miss, Lincs.

TV Bargain

I am a 42-year-old divorced man, and like 'Pauline' of
Somerset in Vol 15 No 2, I have fond memories of cross-
dressing, firstly into my mother's clothes, then my sister's,
then my wife's up until the time we were divorced.

I've seen many changes in fashion over the years, my
favourite being the Fifties, when it was all big circular
skirts and flouncy petticoats. My sister's wardrobe took a
terrible hammering, without her knowledge, as I dressed
up in her rock 'n' roll skirts and billowy petticoats,
rubbing the material against my thighs as I watched myself
wanking in the mirror.

Later in life, after a few years of marriage, my wife
eventually found out about my true tendencies. So we
came to a mutual understanding that she could go out and

get laid by whoever she fancied.

For my part of the bargain, I had a free ticket to her wardrobe, and she even went as far as to buy me dresses, skirts, petticoats, bra and panties, suspender-belts and stockings.

Most of my evenings and weekends, were spent dolled up to the nines in these fineries. Occasionally she would bring home one of her boyfriends and I would busy myself in the kitchen preparing supper for them.

Did it have anything to do with the eventual break up of our marriage? Well, that's another story. . .

'Della', Essex

8. A MESSY BUSINESS

Heavy Petting
Dinner For Two
Punch Drunk
Food For Thought
Fair Fights

Fighting Fit
Girdled Cream?
My Brilliant Korea
All Out Wrestling
Mud Skippers

Heavy Petting

I've been in England for ten years but I'm still a U.S. citizen. I'm twenty-five and twenty-three stone, 330 pounds, nude. I've had your mag for some time and always read the letters. Sometimes you have printed letters about wrestling and I think what I have to recall may interest your readers.

I don't look as heavy as I really am. That's what my sister is always saying. I live with her and her husband. Recently my sister had a party for her work friends, mainly women. I think she was trying to get me matched because there were two really large ladies present. Both in their early twenties, one was about 265 pounds and quite nice, but the other was over 290 pounds and taller than me and a bit on the pushy side. I think she must have had latent bully tendencies the way she was going on. At the end of the party there were just these two women left and my brother-in-law dragged my sister off to bed as a direct hint for these two to go.

The two women started arguing good humouredly, calling one another names until they started tickling each other. The larger woman made the other squirm onto the floor and just sat astride her rump. After reducing her victim to a mass of helpless giggles the fatter woman stayed sitting on her for half an hour and in the end the smaller girl was quite upset. What had started out as a jokey affair had turned serious and she left the house, sobbing to her car.

I told the remaining woman she was a bully, and to pick on someone who could hit back. She hinted that I could be that person and I started to tickle her. I got the jump on her and getting behind her, tickled her so bad she sank to her knees. It's not often someone of my size gets a girl almost the same weight and I was feeling randy, so as she sank to her belly on the floor I just followed her down and sat fairly and squarely astride her big fat arse.

I sank all my weight onto her and when I heard her gasp I tickled her even more. Her dress had ridden up exposing bare thighs, which I tickled and groped. After ten minutes she tried to turn over and threatened all hell upon me when she did. I let her turn under me, pretending to resist, but all the time getting great handfuls of tit. She finally lay on her back with me fully astride her.

There we remained for twenty minutes, silently struggling for victory. It was like laying astride a tubular water bed, but much firmer, and she was wriggling against my old man. She just couldn't buck me off and gradually became exhausted and allowed me to pin her hands over her head. Our faces were close and we kissed like passionate lovers but there was still the element of competition in her eyes. I mean, it isn't often a girl of her size gets beaten. Her heavy breathing lifting me and lowering me massaged my cock and I came off.

She told me I'd won but I told her I had to claim a reward. She didn't want intercourse, but agreed to getting naked for me to have a tit fuck and blow job. Although she was breathless she let me sit astride her chest and rub my cocky between her big mounds till I came again. Then I sat on them while she gobbled me. She could really stand my weight on her and she drank what I had left in me. I hope to see her again soon for another buff-ride.

J.C., West London

Dinner For Two
Reading some of the letters from your readers has prompted me to write to you about an old girlfriend of mine, Tina.

One evening, after a pleasant meal at a local steakhouse, Tina took me back to her flat for coffee. She stopped in the hall and giggling, told me to go and sit down in the living room — but only after I had taken all my clothes off. 'This seems promising,' I thought. It turned out to be even better than I expected.

In the living room all the furniture had been moved up against the walls, and the entire floor had been covered with a polythene sheet. A table was in the centre of the floor, with something on it which was covered with a cloth. I was given strict instructions not to touch anything, and Tina disappeared into her bedroom.

After a wait which seemed like hours, she finally reappeared dressed in a white full-length underslip through which I could make out the lines of a white bra, panties, suspenders and white stockings, all set off by a pair of white high heeled shoes.

With a hint of a smile Tina uncovered the table to reveal several bowls of custard, jellies, large tarts and one huge gateau. Standing beside the table, Tina reached over the far side to pick up one of the tarts. Standing back up straight, I noticed that she had managed to dip her left tit into a bowl of custard. 'Oh dear,' she said as the custard trickled down the front of her slip.

Putting the tart down on the floor, she wiped the custard off her breast with her fingers and then licked them. She then plunged her hand into the custard, again licking her fingers and this time she closed her eyes as if she was about to have an orgasm. Then she repeated the process, this time sitting on the floor on top of the tart. When she stood up the sight of custard running down her slip at the front and the tart sliding down over her bottom and onto her legs was a real turn on.

Grasping the top of the slip with both hands she tore it off, leaving her clean bra and pants in full view. Undoing her white half-cup bra she laid it on the table and poured custard into the cups. Next she held the bra back to her breasts, and I saw the custard ooze around the sides of the bra cups onto her hands and then begin its slide down her naked stomach. She rubbed the custard soaked bra around and around on her tits and then dropped it to the floor. The custard covered parts of her anatomy were then anointed with jelly, which broke up and squelched in a lovely manner. Tina then climbed onto the table, kneeling in a tart in the process. She picked up the gateau. This was it.

Pulling the front of her panties out, she ever so slowly pushed the gateau down inside her knickers. Most of the cake broke up and ended up on the table, but the rest was inside the front of her pants and rested there, forming a huge bulge. Tina's hand pressed down on her crotch and the cream oozed out from the legs of her panties, and slithered down her legs.

I had a rampant hard-on by now and moved towards her. 'Not yet,' she screamed. She then rolled in the remains of the food on the table, moaning as she did so. For a while she went completely crazy on the table on her own, then without warning Tina was beside me and slapped a dollop of cream on my tool — which she then began to lick off. She stood back. What a lovely mess. Cream over her face from the tool job, and the rest of her body and nylons covered in a gooey mess, part of which was running down and dripping off her.

The final fucking took place in the middle of the remains of the custard and jellies, as we rolled around in pleasure. What a session.

Afterwards, before taking a shower we tried to lick each other clean and Tina said: 'If you like that, I've got something else for you next weekend.' And, as it turned out, she certainly had — I might write and tell you about it one day.

Gus, Birmingham

225

Punch Drunk

I get a little angry at letters from men who enjoy seeing us females wrestling, boxing, fighting and cat-fighting. What about us? Do they not think that many of us enjoy seeing *them* fight? Are they prepared to strip off, put the gloves on and fight for our pleasure? I doubt it very much.

I have always enjoyed seeing a good fight, and having one too. When I was at school I attended all the junior boxing tournaments, and if I heard of a fight being arranged after school hours I was certain to be one of the first there.

Several times I had scrappy little fights and tussles with other girls, but it was not until I was 18 that I got the chance I had been waiting for — a real, prearranged 'go'. One evening at a dance I got into a row with a girl I had disliked for a long time, and we arranged to meet the next night to fight it out.

The rest of the evening and the next day I spent in a constant state of excitement. The fight took place with just the two of us alone. I lost, but learned a lot. For example, the pre-fight chat is very important. I remember quite clearly that as she took her coat off she said, 'I've been looking forward to this you bitch, and I've waited too long. Come on then — fight!' There was lots more, but when she said that I thought I was going to swoon with the fantastic feeling it gave me. I'm sure she was as turned on as I was.

Anyway, about the men. I am 28 now, and my live-in fellow loves to fight for me. We are both turned on by boxing gloves, but only once could he get another man to fight him with the gloves on. Then one day we answered an advert in a contact magazine from a couple who wanted a session of sensual boxing. Our problems were over. At last I could see my fellow with the gloves on, and in private, with no interference from anyone.

We now meet two couples on a fairly regular basis. With the original couple it is just a sexy sparring session, but the other couple are a bit different. When we glove up with them it's to really box — and box to win.

So we have the best of both worlds. I can enjoy seeing my man with the gloves on and fighting, and he can watch me as I do the same. Just to see two horny men having it out with the gloves on and naked is such a fantastic turn-on that I orgasm long before it's my turn to get gloved up.

Finally, and what I meant to say in the first place, all you so-called men who want to see women fighting, just remember us females. Do some fighting yourselves. You'd be surprised at the result when your girlfriend or wife shows you what it does for them. Also, nine times out of ten they'll fight for you. Even *with* you. It's the best foreplay I know. So let's see you men doing your share.

One last thing. I rarely use bad language, but during our sessions the really bad words we use during the build up are a very important part, and we women are the worst (or best!). To see and hear the other girl and me as we challenge each other to fight it out, one would expect us to fight to the death. Of course we don't. It's too sexy to last more than two or three rounds anyway.

Sharon, Herts.

Food For Thought

Ever since I can remember, I've had a thing about gooey, creamy foods like jelly, trifle, custard pie and rice pudding. I don't know why but they instantly make my thoughts turn to sexy things. I suppose it's because they're messy and sex is all about secretions and slipperiness, too. I always wanted to be one of those ladies who were hired for special banquets and made to lie on a table and get covered in dessert, delicious things like meringue, ice cream and fruit, and the guests had to lick and suck it off. I've always longed to meet a man who'd shove an ice-cream cornet right up my snatch, then eat it out. Ooh, my innards literally contract and go all trembly at the thought.

Anyway, recently I met a man who's turned out to be

the nearest so far to my idea in that he adores messing around with sexy foods, too. When I confided my kink to him, he said he'd see what he could do.

Next time I visited him, he'd got things well prepared. The bed was covered in a sheet of black polythene and he asked me to strip off and lie on it. Then he went away into the kitchen while I itched and ached in anticipation. When he came back, he was holding a small jug.

'Close your eyes,' he ordered. I obeyed and felt a wonderful warm, thick liquid blobbing onto my tits, my belly-button and being poured between my legs. It aroused me incredibly. He said I could open my eyes . . . and I found I was covered with a thick brown sauce which he said was a special hazelnut liqueur he'd bought in Austria. I lay there quivering while he licked it all off, making absolutely sure that not a sticky drop remained on my hard, jutting nipples, in my navel or around my cunt.

Then he disappeared again, then came back telling me to prepare myself for a shock. I braced myself and gasped as he poured a stream of thin, frozen cream right down from my neck to my crotch. As a *pièce de résistance*, he produced four strawberries and placed them strategically, one on each nipple, one in my belly-button and one just above my clitoris. Slowly circling each nipple with his tongue, he nibbled off the strawberries, then sucked the one from my navel.

His cock was huge and swollen and nudged me in the stomach, where it got covered in cream. I bent forward, sucked it gently into my mouth and licked off the cool, sweet coating, delighting in the taste of his own juice mingling with the cream.

When his head came down and ate the strawberry off my crotch, I was beside myself, squirming and moaning. The cream by now had run into all my crevices and Paul set himself the task of running his tongue everywhere, inside and out. Some of the cream and liqueur had trickled underneath me and I was slithering on the polythene, feeling its delicious wet, stickiness on my back and bottom.

Paul still hadn't finished, though. He produced a tube of soft, rich cream, again acquired abroad, and squeezed it out on me, writing the word 'Fuck' across my stomach! Then he poised himself above me and lowered himself onto me and I had the satisfaction of feeling the cream squish and spread between our bodies.

He fucked me with his cream-covered cock. We slid about on the polythene sheet — because it was black, the streaks of white cream showed up beautifully. Every time his balls banged against my bottom, they stuck to it slightly which really turned me on. My tits slithered all over his chest. We squirmed about, spreading the goo all over each other, rolling in it. I shuddered in orgasm after orgasm.

When he groaned that he was coming, I grabbed his cock, pulled it out of me, held it in the air, wanked it furiously and saw, to my absolute delight, his streams and gobbets of white spunk spattering all over the black plastic.

It was the best and messiest screw of my life. Next time someone offers me 69, I'm going to say, 'No, I'd prefer a 99, chocolate stick and all!'

Jean, Shropshire

Fair Fights

I think there is nothing more exciting than the sight of two well-developed girls slogging it out in a boxing ring or on a wrestling mat.

My girlfriend is a keen amateur wrestler, having been introduced to it while attending keep-fit classes, and we have travelled together all over the Midlands where she has private bouts — blondes, brunettes, and quite a few coloured girls too.

Jill is a very well-developed girl, 5′ 6″ tall with a 38″ bust. She wrestles in a brief blue leotard and wrestling boots, but if her opponent agrees she will fight topless. I act as her second, and her opponent's husband usually does the same.

During a hard fight she perspires a lot and I have to wipe her down between rounds. The usual arrangement is that after each fight the second takes his wrestler to bed — and boy, do we have sex then!

Jill has also had one boxing match and enjoyed it greatly, but finding opponenents is difficult, especially after what happened at that match.

We found a willing female opponent in Birmingham, and we arrived at her house in the 'stockbroker belt' to be greeted by her husband and sister. We all had drinks first and got to know one another. Valerie, the opponent, suggested to Jill that they went up to her bedroom to change, while we went into the lounge, which had been rigged up with an excellent boxing ring. Valerie's husband said that this was her tenth bout and that she had won eight of them.

Half an hour later the girls came down, looking gorgeous in satin trunks, boxing boots and white gloves. Valerie's sister acted as her second and looked very sexy in tight tee shirt and jeans, and her husband was referee.

In the first round Jill got in some good punches and towards the end Valerie was beginning to get hurt. But in the second round Valerie got Jill in the corner and pummelled her body, Jill's face creased with pain, but she caught Valerie with a right uppercut, sending her down for a count of eight.

In the third round, Jill was over-powering Valerie, but she was fighting back well and both the girls were wet with sweat by the end of the round. Jill knocked Valerie all round the ring in the fourth and it was surprising that she lasted to the end of the round. Her right eye was swollen and her nose was bleeding.

Valerie insisted in fighting on to a fifth round, but in the first minute she went down three times and her husband stopped the fight, declaring Jill the winner.

Both girls embraced one another to show no hard feelings, though I must say that I had them!

After patching up Valerie and bathing Jill's swollen cheek, we all went up to bed for a terrific night of sex. While I was having it off with Valerie she told me that Jill had a great future in boxing and should go to America to do it professionally, which she later did. She is now in training for her first fight over there, and I'm looking for another girl to train.

D.H., Gloucestershire

Fighting Fit

Following your super article on Candy Samples in Vol. 18 No. 1 (surely one of the most perfectly formed creatures ever), would it be possible to run a similar feature on the equally superb Uschi Digard? As a keen follower of women's wrestling, as seem to be a lot of your readers, I wonder if it would be possible to feature some of the films in which Candy and Uschi have wrestled together.

When I worked in the USA a couple of years back, there was a firm producing and hiring films, one of which was a wrestling tournament filmed in a plush night club. The standard of wrestling was quite good — most such films are obviously faked — and in all three matches the contestants wore very skimpy bikinis. Two elimination matches were followed by the final.

The wrestling was conducted to American rules, i.e. no rounds, contestants breaking only after a fall, with one pin-fall deciding the eliminators and two falls the final.

In the first bout Candy Samples was matched against a woman of equally statuesque proportions called Tammi Roche, and after a good clean contest Candy pinned her opponent with a crosspress using her bear hug to weaken her first. Uschi Digard wrestles under the name of Uschi Dansk and she was matched against a Brazilian girl, Isabel Sarli, in her eliminator.

231

Her match was much harder fought than the Samples/ Roche contest, with both women handing out rough punishment. Sarli had her opponent in trouble a couple of times with some vicious stomach punches (allowed under US rules), but Uschi emerged the victor after some twenty minutes grappling when she pinned Sarli, after kneeing her in the stomach to weaken her.

Uschi then met Candy in the final bout. Candy wore a flashy silver bikini and Uschi a plain black one, and in terms of height, weight and build they appeared well matched.

Surprisingly though, Uschi pinned Samples quite easily, twice inside ten minutes, to win. I must admit to being surprised at the level of skill exhibited by all the women in this particular film.

Another tape that I saw features a fight, and the word 'fight' is used deliberately, between Annie Ample and Kitten Natividad. This was billed as a special challenge match and was to be decided on submissions. Both women were introduced to the crowd, grudgingly shook hands and went to their corners. When they removed their robes, or in Kitten's case, mink coat, they were totally nude.

Quite early on, Kitten forced Annie to submit to a bear hug across her breasts, then the contest became a real fight with both women taking some punishment in the breast area. Kitten seemed to be just on top until she tried to body check Annie by bouncing off the ropes, but she met Annie's knees, taking it full in the stomach and quickly submitting to a body scissors, allowing her opponent to equalise.

Kitten never recovered, and the end came when Annie clamped the same move on her stomach. Judging by the pressure marks on both their bodies, it wasn't a put up job either.

Lastly, I have seen adverts for a film which features a topless contest between Uschi Digart and Candy Samples and was filmed, I think, by Russ Meyer. Could Fiesta possibly find out the result and perhaps run a few photos from the film — or maybe a girl wrestling photo feature?

Kevin, Leeds

Girdled Cream?

In the last Fiesta Holiday Special you featured the lovely Doris Crunge in Sunny Side Up, which ended with Doris pouring custard over a holiday guest called Roy. What I would like to see, and I am sure lots of other readers would as well, is Doris in a slapstick or mud wrestling scene.

Perhaps it could go like this. Roy decides to get his revenge and pours a bucket of custard over Doris, who is fully clothed, and then a bucket of cream. After this he pulls Doris's dress off to reveal her in underwear, and continues to give her the custard and cream treatment.

This goes on until she is completely naked and he is plastering her lovely tits. Perhaps she covers him in it too. Oh, please a million times see what you can do. I am certain sales would break a world record.

I.P., Devon

My Brilliant Korea

What a great surprise it was seeing a photo of Silky Sam in Fiesta, after all these years. He's the nude wrestler showing his all in Vol. 17 No. 3. Well known to the lads at Mokpo medical base, and I well remember those naughty nurses, the enema wallahs of Mokpo, and stations East. The nurses gave Silky Sam the name because his skin really was smooth and gleamed like silk. How do I know? When he came strutting along the rows of seats, me and the boys would have a feel of his muscles, rub his bum, and squeeze the cheeks, all for a laugh, of course, Little Jimmy (where is he now?) gave him the 'Cough' treatment one night, the little sod.

I would love to meet the lads again, if only to talk about *that night*. I am sure that your correspondent must have been present on *that night* as she coyly mentions flatus, probably hoping to jog a few memories. But flatus was not what we called it. Was she the coy little blonde, who sat quietly fluttering her eyelids, but taking it all in just the same? She has certainly jogged my memory, because of all the things I have ever seen, *that night* was the greatest. It stuck out like a, like a, well, stiff thingummy.

The photo doesn't do Silky justice. He was well over six feet tall, and must have weighed sixteen stones, with a superb physique. His cock was thick and about seven inches long slack, and covered in knobbly veins as thick as pencils. His knob was the *pièce de resistance*. I have never seen one anywhere near as big before or since, even in Fiesta. It was about three inches across the breadth, and about the size of a small orange. It was goose-fleshed, pale mauve and shiny, and the eyehole hàd prominent lips like labia majora. You could look straight up the eyehole, which was like the Blackwall tunnel, because it was more to the front of his knob, than at the tip like a normal human being, which he was not. It was no exaggeration to say that you could have shoved a ball pen up his eyehole and he wouldn't have noticed.

His bollocks were the size of duck eggs, and you could have used his scrotum for a bathing cap, beach bag, holdall, etc. There was not a hair on the horizon anywhere. Silky's cock must have been circumcised at least a dozen times and you couldn't help noticing. The flange of his knob stuck out like the rim of a soup bowl, and his foreskin had been cut right back to his belly button, so that the whole set up was a fashionable shade of violet, tastefully finished in a shiny mauve knob. I believe they used Silky's foreskin as a marquee at big functions.

We lads had attended the wrestling on several occasions, and I well remember the first night that the British and American nurses turned up in the hall, because it was *that night* which showed Silky Sam for what he was, the Flasher Supreme. It was also the night he gained his famous nickname, and since nurses are handling skin all the time, they were quick to christen him. However, since it was obvious that Silky Sam appeared *that night* for the first time naked before European ladies, it was understandable that he should have become over-wrought. His Korean beauties gave him tactile pleasure, poking, stroking, prodding and squeezing his muscles, but some of the nurses were gorgeous. It was summer. They wore scanty white shorts, and yards of shapely white calves and thighs could do things to a healthy lad.

On *that night* everyone, including the nurses, had taken their seats, and a fanfare announced the entry of the gladiators. At the back of the hall, the first wrestler made his appearance. It was Silky, of course, and he was wearing his working clothes, i.e. stark bollock naked. Funny thing was, we lads had got as used to it as the Koreans. We went for the wrestling. Everyone turned in their seats, as was customary, and the nurses, who obviously had not anticipated that this was to be a full frontal affair, fell out of their seats, and we heard one say, amid their giggles; 'Geeze, that's hellish rude!'

Among the American Nurses were four black girls, and these appeared to be having multiple orgasms.

Silky, spotting the acres of white and brown female flesh, and deciding on a change from the equally appealing fawn coloured female flesh, which was his usual ration, made a beeline for the nursing ranks, skidding to a halt before a delectable dish with gobbler's lips. Even then, his cock was acting suspiciously, for a droplet of love juice oozed from his knob and dangled in an elastic cord from the tip. The nurses, indulging now in a nudge, nudge, wink wink routine, must have noticed on their mental Report Boards; 'Patient undergoing buff examination. Penis flaccid but emitted about 10cc of fluid . . .'

There must have been about twenty or so nurses present on *that night*, and when Silky Sam invited them

235

each to be his guest in a muscle kneading orgy, and after a preliminary pushing at each other in jocular mood, the nurses dutifully squeezed his thighs, calves, and other bulging bits, and the scene really got going. During all this, the girls remained seated, unmoved by the fact that Silky's cock was dangling and drooling about a foot in front of their faces as he moved down the row.

When he got to the black nurses it became evident that they had conspired to see just how much Silky could take. Not much, it transpired, though more than me. There were four black girls, and whilst two remained seated, squeezing his thigh muscles and stroking their hands up and down his thighs, moving high so that their fingertips brushed his bollocks, the other two girls had got to their feet and were running their hands over his body, massaging and kneading his bum, back, belly, bald chest, sides, and even tickling his bald armpits. This bawdy and saucy behaviour delighted the Korean audience as well as us, and they whistled, cheered, applauded, stamped feet, and generally approved.

The lads and myself were getting half hard watching this, brief as it was, but we would never have had the guts to experience that in public. The show was short lived, however. The girls had worked on Silky for not much more than half a minute, and already the volcano was erupting. His great cock suddenly reared up from its launching pad, and for a few seconds stuck straight out, wagging up and down like the jib of a crane, or as if beating time. Then, with another surge of blood and passion, it went on the full horn, even belittling it's first effort, and swung upwards and against his belly with an audible slap, pointing threateningly at his chin. It remained in this position, fully horned up, and about ten inches long. The practice nurses have in army hospitals of pinching buffed soldiers' bums to deflate their horns would not have worked here. Silky's bum would have needed pinching with a mechanical shovel.

For the first time my curiosity, and I've no doubt the

curiosity of everyone in the hall, was satisfied to see how big Silky's dong was on the bonk. Ten inches was a reasonable and conservative estimate. To the Korean girls, it must have seemed like ten feet. Of course, the Korean girls were quite used to naked wrestlers, but I noticed their slit eyes widened when Silky got the horn. Also, for the first time, we had a first class view of the underside. His whole cock and knob had become a dark mauve now, and the veins were hard, bumpy, and almost black. The piss tube stood out in a hard muscular ridge like a drainpipe, and you could count his heartbeats in the violent throb as his cock jerked forward, then back against his belly.

The eyehole was now gaping wide, its lips hard and pouting, and copious squirts of fluid oozed and gushed out, streaming down the shaft and drenching his bollocks, which were rising and falling like yo-yos. Saliva drooled forth, running down his chin, his eyes were popping, and he was groaning. All this was happening partly simultaneously, and partly in rapid succession, but my trained military eye took in all the detail, as I've no doubt my companions and the nurses did. At this stage, the four girls were still running their hands lightly over Silky, although all told for less than a minute, when his hips began to sway back and forth in the familiar rhythmical copulatory movement, signifying the Grande Finale.

The whole crowd had now moved round to a position where they were facing Silky for the showdown, which was now inevitable, and it was fair to say that by now there wasn't a dry pair of knickers in the hall. My own underpants were a bit moist. The girls now moved back a few feet, for they could see that Silky's cock was in its death throes. An amazing phenomenon which was apparent to everybody was that Silky's skin was now a mass of huge goose pimples from head to toe, and if anything, that was the most arresting aspect of the whole thing bar the finish. He was virtually transformed into a fawn coloured lizard. The cheeks of his arse were quivering now like a jelly, probably trying to shake the goose pimples off.

He had placed his hands behind his head to facilitate the girls' tickling of his armpits, and now he kept them there, as the thrusting movements of his hips sped up, and his bum became a quivering blur. He slowly rose up on tiptoe, covered in sweat, his thigh muscles bulging like knots in girders, nipples protruding like cigar butts, and ejaculate now jetting out in gooey blobs, running with the sweat. Although the Korean ladies and gentlemen were already aware of it, it dawned on us, and upon the nurses, that at these very last seconds, what we were witnessing was nothing less than blatant masturbation without the hand, thinly disguised as the traditional and customary wrestling dance which was performed without an erection.

The standing on tiptoe, thighs spread the flexing and unflexing of the thigh muscles, the jerking of the hips to translate the up and down bollock movement into a to and fro swing where they thumped against the thighs, jerking the taut penis, were all contributing to the fast approaching ejaculation. Only a man who had his entire penis skin removed could masturbate in this manner, since, with a skin, even in erection, there is enough elasticity to allow vigorous bollock movement without undue plucking action upon the penis. Everybody present knew that they were watching Silky wanking off over the nurses, but the fact that his modus masturbari resembled a ritual dance spared them the charge of indelicacy. They could argue that they were watching the fleshy poetry of his rippling thigh muscles, but in reality all eyes were glued to the great glistening shaft, waiting for it to vomit. For those of a genteel disposition, in medical parlance, the pelvic copulatory movements induced a reciprocal movement in the scrotum and testes which, in passing in a rearward arc between the thighs, exerted a stress (pulling action, in this case, as if the non-existent foreskin was being forcefully drawn back) upon the cutis vera of the penis, made taut by exposure due to removal of the entire epidermis. In the forward arc of the scrotal movement,

238

the stress was relieved. Rapid and continuous repetition of this two stroke sequence would produce the sensation of an invisible hand firmly masturbating the penis. One could therefore understand why Silky surrendered his cock to such drastic and unsightly treatment. He could literally jerk it off without touching it.

Here he was on *that night* taking himself in hand without taking himself in hand, and the naughty nurses of Mokpo Medical Base were loving it. I don't suppose they fancied Silky's cock, it was like a big lump of raw meat, but it was fun watching it. Naturally, as he was jerking to a finish, his eyes were glued to the array of naked white female legs (nurses for the use of) spread before him, and he must have been fantasising like mad in his obvious frustration.

Where there had been cheering and so on, there was now a deathly silence broken only by Silky panting and grunting. All of this takes longer to describe than it actually took to happen, but now comes the part that A.H. coyly refers to in her letter. The silence was broken, nay, shattered, by a broadside of raucous farts, rich and juicy, exploding from Silky's muscular arse in rapid succession and echoing round the hall like gunfire, rattling the windows, scorching his fat cheeks, and generally causing havoc. This was the fanfare heralding the Moment of Glory.

The black girls had made a covenant and Silky was honouring it. He was mentally devouring the milky white thighs before him, getting the cheapest of cheap thrills, when he let rip a string of wet farts (reminding the nurses of enemas!) and his cock threw up. All eyes were on the purple elephant's trunk, and we virtually saw Silky's thread bulging up the piss tube on his vertical cock, like footballs whizzing up the inside of some snake, and there it was. At the very last moment his eyehole gaped open even wider, and with the overhead lights shining down on it, you could bloody nigh see his bollocks at the other end. He was farting in ecstasy when the first great shot of thick

239

spunk vomitted out of his cock and shot up his belly to splurge between his tits, closely followed by a second load which on it's way up filled his belly button, and ended up drooping from his nipples like a pearl necklace. The third and final splurge was weaker, getting a few inches from his knob, then falling back and slithering off down his left thigh, like the proverbial white mouse.

During the actual ejaculation, everybody was shrieking with laughter, including the nurses, who were calling out all sorts of things by way of banter. The word 'flasher' was not commonly used then (34 years ago) so Silky was a cheap thrill cheat. 'Quick, grab a bed bottle,' cried one, and 'Don't wipe it up, shovel it up!' said another, as Silky's hips came gradually to a halt, and he stood there looking like a cup of whitewash had been thrown at him.

The eight American nurses were in overnight transit, moving North the next day, and although the British nurses continued their cock watching, we never had quite the same bawdy goings on again. Silky Sam must have had many a juicy wank thinking about *that night*. Probably still does.

Thanks for the memory, A.H. Your hints of flatus and enemas tells me that you were there *that night*. I'd love to know what you really thought about what happened, you were near enough with the other girls to taste it.

Sergeant W., Kent

All Out Wrestling
Sorting through some personal papers recently, I discovered some negatives which date back to when I was a nurse during the Korean war. The first time that I, and several of the other girls at the base hospital visited a wrestling contest, we were very amused to find that it was the custom for the contestants to wrestle in their birthday suits. Before each contest, all of the participants would strut and posture in the nude, flexing their muscles as they

240

moved amongst the audience, and the local ladies clamoured to feel the firmness of bicep, thigh and calf. We nurses, contemplating at close quarters various rippling buttocks, were reminded of enemas, jabs and other buttocky things.

During the contests, the ladies and gentlemen of the audience beseech their particular hero to emasculate his opponent as the combatants, with fingers sunk deeply into each others rumps, attempt a throw. One qualification of being a Korean wrestler appeared to be the ability for producing a *raucus flatus*, which invariably brought a cheer from the crowd.

One of the contestants kindly posed for my camera, naked and proud, flexing his muscles and posturing, inviting us to feel his muscles, which were certainly very hard. This particular gentleman was completely hairless all over, no doubt from alopecia, and his face, as were the faces of the other wrestlers, was painted pink.

As a nurse, I particularly noted two things. One was that he had a beautifully smooth and clear skin, and the other was that he had been circumcised in such a way that the entire skin of the penis had ben removed, leaving it rather raw looking and veiny. Altogether, with his pink painted face and his mauve penis, he made a bizarre sight.

We later visited further wrestling contests, and sometimes the wrestlers were very fat, but always naked, and often the contest was one of penis pulling and testicle twisting. After those market place battles, British wrestling is so predictable. Perhaps this photo would make one for the oriental ladies.

A.H., Essex

Mud Skippers
It was a great joy for my wife and I to see the lovely pictures of Mandy (Vol 16 No 3). We have both been aware of the eroticism of mud-larking for many years, but

had despaired of seeing it given more than the most derisory coverage in any of the mass-circulation magazines.

Of course we have a few acquaintances who share our particular interest, or 'kink' as I suppose we should call it. But for some reason the world seems to be unable to accept us, even while it condones other practices far more unusual.

Sometimes, like Mandy in the pictures, my wife and I indulge while wearing ordinary clothes, while at other times we dress ourselves in special rubber outfits which we obtained specifically for 'larking'. We are lucky enough to live within reasonable driving distance of beautiful mud pools, and so are able to indulge ourselves whenever the mood takes us and the weather is clement.

M.A.S., Berks.

9. WORD OF MOUTH

Parky Weather

Chopped Ham

A Gentleman
And A Swallow

Cork Screw

Swallow Tale

Forfeits For Photographs

Non-Dairy Produce

In Praise Of Lust

More Military Cuts

Hands That Do Dishes

Tongue Tied

In The Deep End

Parky Weather

My girlfriend really enjoys reading magazines while we screw, and Fiesta always makes her especially randy. I always know when she's in the mood for a good fucking, because when we pass a newsagents she'll stop outside and gaze longingly at the sex literature. Usually she waits outside while I go in and choose something, but if there's a female shop assistant Sally's not adverse to buying it herself.

By this stage she'll usually be pretty turned on and flushed with excitement, and, if it's sunny, insist on going to the local park. This gives her a chance for a spot of exhibitionism. Sally finds a potential audience (not difficult for a 19 year old 5′ 8″ redhead!) and sits facing them with her legs apart, her knickers on full view and her mini-skirt rucked up around her waist. This is always done so as to *appear* totally casual, since this adds to her excitement. She always leaves a great deal of unshaven hair around her cunt so as to present a really stimulating sight. She generally wears a small pair of pale-coloured cotton panties which cling more and more tightly to her fanny-lips as her vaginal juices start to flow. Her clitty stands out quite visibly once the sticky wet patch has started to appear and the effect is incredible!

At this point we usually end up french kissing and stroking each other. I often can't resist running my hands up Sally's thighs and tracing the outline of her soaking hole — an act that is invariably appreciated by our spectators. By this stage it's time to go home.

Once home Sally always grabs the dirty mag and lies face-down on the hearth-rug, her right hand halfway up her fanny, desperate to relieve herself. She never undresses, finding it 'dirtier' to wank fully clothed. Sally always loves it if I stand and ejaculate over her. She likes to rub my semen into her dress, T-shirt and hair. Although my passion usually subsides for a time after this, Sally is just starting, and after a while her moans and obscenities have me worked up again. She loves me to do things that some people would consider distasteful. I'll take off her knickers and smell and suck the juice-stained crotch, all the time masturbating for her benefit and she finds my habit of licking the hairy area around her anus really exciting.

She likes me to leave conspicuous love-bites on her neck and breasts — she works as a checkout girl at a supermarket and she finds the subsequent randy looks she gets from male customers a real turn-on. Sally tells me that she often has to slope off to the staff toilet and have a quick wank so as to relieve the tension.

I'm writing this letter just to indicate the sort of things Sally and I (two average young people) get up to. There are lots more things that I could tell you about, but first let's hear from more of the under 25's.

Ian, Chesterfield

Chopped Ham

As a forty year old history teacher you would probably think me prim and prudish, but like my husband Mark, I was intrigued by the letters connecting penile removal and cunnilingus ('Pussy Talk' and 'Sliced Pork') — although my initial thought of all those chopped off willies was, 'Ugh! What a waste.'

Research during my student days taught me that ancient history contains more sex, lust and kinky goings-on than any modern porno video. The more sexually minded a people were, the more they tried to stop their foes enjoying sexual pleasure. Nevertheless, penile removal —

although mentioned in 'The Perfumed Garden' — was extremely rare compared with the removal of the testicles.

This was probably because it carried such a high mortality rate that it was sometimes regarded as the equivalent of the more customary practice of executing all the men.

Like testical removal, it naturally prevented men from reproducing, and no doubt chauvinistic conquerors felt that it gave them an advantage in scoring with the local ladies. Its principal aim was to ensure that the victims' only sexual activity would be cunnilingus, and that they would endure frustration which could never be relieved. Any nation whose males regarded women as inferior and cunnilingus as degrading for a man, were, therefore, ideal candidates for the chop.

In the terms 'Greek Cut' and 'Greek Kiss', the cut obviously refers to those who did the cutting and the kiss to those on the receiving end. The Greek part appears contradictory at first, but refers to an ancient Greek civil war.

The ancient Greeks were unlucky, for some decades later one of their city colonies fell to the Carthaginians who cut off every adult penis, despite a passionate plea from the local Guild of Prostitutes who feared for their livelihood after the Carthaginians' departure.

One of my student friends used to speculate on the social and psychological impact of JT removal, on both men and women, and wondered how the men disposed of their semen. If I had still known her four years ago, I could have supplied her with some first hand data to assist with her speculation.

Mark had to be circumcised to cure some foreskin trouble, and the scars took longer than expected to heal. He was given drugs to curb his sex drive, which he foolishly stopped taking. As his penis was sore and raw, intercourse and masturbation were impossible, and when he begged me for sex, I ended up with his head between my legs, with him making a pig of himself much to my delight. Being cunnie-sucked regularly seemed to make me produce more jelly, all of which Mark lapped up greedily.

Orgasm for him was obviously impossible but he felt that, during a sucking session, satisfaction was just around the corner. Eventually, he entered a vicious circle. The more he sucked me off, the more he became frustrated and tried to relieve this with more sucking-off. Even when his frustration temporarily subsided, it would flare up again at the sight of a skirt lifted by the breeze or even on seeing can-can girls on television. (He has a thing about the can-can.)

He suffered from depression, and even dreamt that he was enjoying intercourse, only to wake up to find that he had copiously discharged his fluids without any satisfaction. Sometimes he woke me up three times in a night for a suck, all of which was a terrible strain on both of us.

To all intents and purposes, Mark was a man with no penis whose balls were ruling his life. Thankfully, his scars healed and we were able to enjoy intercourse again.

Incidentally, I adore being cunny-sucked, but regard it as a sexy, spicy extra, and not a substitute for a penis. I think I would just about get by if it had to be the only permanent method of lovemaking. Let's hope, ladies, that we never have to find out what life would be like, and that the Russians haven't got some special kind of laser weapon that whips off willies en masse!

Nicky, Nottingham

A Gentleman And A Swallow

What a thrill it was to read Gerald of Derbyshire's letter in Fiesta Vol. 18 No. 5 in which he describes how his wife Anne joined him in the Gents in the park to read the graffiti. Before reading Gerald's letter I thought that I was unique in having been into a Gents.

My husband is a lecturer and often, after a hard day,

when walking home through the park he will call in the Gents for a little relaxation. He'd often told me about the graffiti and always described his experiences in there.

One night in bed I told him that I'd love to visit the Gents. He immediately said, 'Why not. You could easily pass for a young lad.' I have quite small breasts and my hair is quite short.

The following afternoon I put on jeans and roll neck jumper and we set out for the park. John, my husband, had given me detailed instructions as to what I should do, and it was arranged that he would stand at the urinal whilst I entered one of the two cubicles. The door to the cubicle has a hole in it so that I could be in visual contact with John. Also, the dividing wall of the cubicle had a very large hole in it. Just as Gerald described in his letter, the back of the door was covered in grafitti.

I was enjoying myself reading the stories when I heard someone enter the other cubicle. I looked through the hole in the door and John gave me the thumbs up sign, so I immediately sat on the toilet seat. As John had instructed me, I moved my arm as if a man masturbating. It worked like a charm. A note was pushed through the hole in the wall asking me to drop my trousers and stand up? I did so, but presenting my bum to him of course. I had my panties on but John had said that didn't matter as lots of men liked wearing undies.

Then I sat on the seat again, as John had instructed, and put my finger briefly through the hole. It was fantastic. The man in the other cubicle pushed his prick through the hole. I've seen and played with lots of pricks of course; but what I found was that having a prick isolated as it were from its owner I was able to really enjoy looking at it without any other distractions. I started to stroke it and was fascinated to see the knob swell up to such an extent that it became shiny. Then I saw the pee-hole open and I quickly bent down and took his length into my mouth just in time to receive his first jet which I swallowed — ambrosia!! He withdrew his prick then and quickly left.

John had seen everything. It had made him so randy that he couldn't wait to get home and there and then he turned me with my back to a tree and lovingly fucked me. I wonder if other women have had similar experiences in Gents? I'd love to be able to write to them to exchange experiences as John and I have often been back to that Gents. It's great fun.

Hazel, West Country

Cork Screw

I would like to tell you of an experience I had four years ago. It all started when I was taking a vacation course during the long holiday period. The first lesson was over and the class was ready to see who was to take us in English. Five minutes after the previous lesson had ended a lady entered the classroom and said she was to take us for English through the six week course. She introduced herself as Lynn. The immediate sight of this nicely shaped lady made me get a hard-on. Throughout the whole English lesson I kept looking at this lady, but was not listening to what she was saying. I was thinking of something else — I fancied her as my girlfriend.

The rest of the six lessons took me through a dream, thinking of her. Three days later I tried to give up thinking of her because, since she first struck my sight I never made any progress academically.

Two weeks later Lynn got to know that I had been looking at her all through her teachings. So one day after a lesson with us, which was the last lesson of the day, she asked me to help her carry some scripts to her car. On the way she asked: 'What is it that is so extraordinary about me that keeps you looking at me whenever I am teaching?' This question nearly made me sink into the ground.

At first I had wanted to lie, but at last I told her, her shape was so attractive that I could not give up looking at her. She smiled at my answer. She drove me in her car and showed me her house, and asked me to come over to her house for lunch after classes the next day.

She was off duty the next day. Soon after classes I took a cab to her house which was a couple of kilometres from the college. I was really surprised when I got there. She had laid the table like a romantic chinese restaurant, she had cooked a fantastic meal and we had a lot of whisky. She wore a light blue gown, through which I could see her beautiful body. After lunch I sat on the sofa to read a mag, which I took from her centre table. She brought me a glass of whisky and sat next to me on the sofa. Her large round boobs made me have a hard-on, and I kept looking at them out of the corner of my eye. Then she turned round and said, 'Do you really think I look beautiful?' I said yes, then she slipped her arm behind my head and before I realised we were kissing. Her tongue nearly filled my mouth.

Lynn started rubbing a hand over my chest and next she started undoing my buttons one by one. All the time, her other hand was behind my head, stroking my hair. She went really wild. She was literally crushing my lips. At this point I started to get stiff, so I tried to point my cork upwards without her noticing. But she noticed and offered to help me with it, then she started sliding her lips over my chest, then my stomach while all the time holding my testicles and the base of the cork.

Lynn cupped my cork with her mouth and started sucking. This sent me wild. She sucked my cork until I had exploded and finished. When I regained strength, I took one of her boobs and started sucking the nipple till she got wild. I then moved on to her pussy and sucked her till she was moaning. She asked me to stop so that we could move to the bedroom.

When we got to the bedroom, we started kissing and I could feel myself getting stiff again, as my hands were roaming all over Lynn's beautiful body — over her breasts and those hard nipples, and down to her pussy. It was

250

bushy. I literally had to rummage round for her crack, but when I found it, it was very damp there and Lynn let out a gasp as I pushed my finger into her.

She kept moaning as I slid my finger in and out, but after a couple of minutes she gently pushed away my hand and lay back on the bed with legs wide apart. She said: 'I want to feel your cork inside me,' so I moved onto her and my erection easily slipped in.

This was the first time I had ever slid my cork into a pussy without using a condom. I was glad I had come earlier on because it gave me more staying power.

I think Lynn must have orgasmed three times before we both came together in one final orgasm. Then we both lay on the bed exhausted. We had intercourse three additional times before I left her house.

All night I lay in bed, hardly able to believe that had happened between my English teacher of twenty-six and me, a student of eighteen. Since that afternoon's experience she smiles to me any time she is in our class, and has often invited me to her house for a fuck.

Crazy Morgan, Ghana

Swallow Tale

Reading in a recent issue of Fiesta about someone wanking whilst looking in the mirror and coming into his own mouth has prompted me to tell you about my method.

I switch the tape recorder to record and then give a running commentary while I masturbate. I describe how I am rubbing my prick and then when I am ready to come I pull my legs over my head and rest my feet on the settee so that my prick is pointing down towards my mouth.

I then rub slowly until I come, and as my hot creamy spunk shoots into my mouth I make sure that I slurp and swallow loudly. Later I play the recording to my wife who thinks it's great. She listens intently to all the details, especially when I come. My wife always likes to see me come and her favourite method is to get me to lie on the bed and to pull my feet over my head and rest them on the headboard. She then kneels down on the bed behind me so that she can look down between my legs and see my prick pointing towards my mouth. She rubs my prick with her right hand and opens my mouth with her left.

She masturbates me slowly and when I reach a climax, she aims my come into my mouth. She rubs until she has milked the last drop, and she really enjoys it.

Terry, Herts.

Forfeits For Photographs

I write to tell you how much my wife (Fay of York, Fiesta 16/11) and I enjoyed this particular issue of your magazine. She had not previously posed for you but she was delighted with the pictures and her response made me ecstatic. But I feel I must tell you what I had to go through in order to persuade her to sit for them in the first place.

Basically, she demanded to be fucked in a variety of ways. We had both taken the day off work and it was my wife's idea to spend most of it in bed. I agreed without much of a struggle and straight away, she began to fondle my 8½" prick. She warned me in advance that after she had finished with me, Linda Lovelace's exploits would seem tame.

She began her threat by exposing her 46" tits and rubbing them along the entire length of my body. When she arrived at my huge prick, which was actually throbbing with anticipation at this point, she opened her gorgeous mouth and took in the tip between her lips. Very slowly, she absorbed its entire length, pausing at each inch to ensure that I did not get too excited to start with. The she worked up a furious rhythm, driving me to the edge of frenzy. Both of us were panting heavily, and between breaths, I asked her if she was prepared to be photographed for Fiesta. She agreed that it would be exciting, but first I was to pay certain forfeits.

Firstly, I was to come fully in her mouth. (*Some forfeit — Ed.*) Taking my silence for assent, she reached down to my prick again and repeated the lovely slow movements of before until she had completely enveloped it. I warned her that I was about to come, for I felt the spunk moving towards the glans, but she was in no mood to pay attention. She held on tightly with her mouth glued to my stem. Then I couldn't hold back any longer. I must have shot my load right down the back of her throat.

Secondly, she suggested that we went downstairs. Still eager to photograph her beautiful figure, I begged her to strip. She responded immediately by stripping off altogether and lying back on the kitchen table with her legs wide open, urging me to make her come with my tongue. I opened her legs as wide as possible, thrust my tongue deep into her cunt and started to explore her interior.

She was soon writhing in ecstasy. The juice was just pouring out of her. Soon I felt her 'come' spreading along my face, as she shouted that she was orgasming. Having recovered from this kitchen scene, I was told that there was still one thing outstanding before I could get out the camera. She demanded that I get out the razor and shave off her pubic hair.

While I went off to locate it, she slipped into a hot bath. I had to stand back and admire her glistening naked body in the water, covered in pink suds. With loving care, I proceeded to shave her thatch until the mound was utterly smooth. But, thinking I had carried out each forfeit perfectly, I was in for one more surprise. She was still not satisfied.

She insisted that I should strip off again, jump in the bath with her and fuck her under the water. As I did so, she told me that when I felt I was about to ejaculate, I should withdraw from her cunt and splash my spunk over her tits and face. Sure enough, when the pressure at the base of my balls was too much for me to contain, I quickly drew out my cock. Just as I was about to spurt, Fay grabbed my stalk wrapped her tits around it and rubbed until I shot all over her mouth, nose, eyes and cheeks. Some of it even landed in her hair.

At this point, she informed me that she was ready for a photo session. I only hope you enjoyed the results as much as we did. Comments would be appreciated.

J. of York

Non-Dairy Produce

In your Vol. 17 No. 7 issue, a couple of male correspondents make fleeting references to milk from a woman's breasts. I wonder how many of your readers have known the sheer excitement of keeping a woman in milk for a prolonged period of time?

Some three years ago I met a young woman in a disco. I learned during the course of the evening that she was unmarried, but had a six month old baby son at home. As the evening progressed, she confessed that she was reluctantly going to have to wean him — reluctantly, she explained, because she got so much pleasure from being suckled.

With an eye to the main chance, I told her that as soon as she took her baby off the breast, she would automatically stop producing milk, and that if she wished to continue having firm, round breasts full of milk, she would need to carry on having them suckled regularly twice a day. I took over from the baby that very night.

Thereafter, either at her place or mine, we met twice a day, and twice a day I would empty each breast of its milk. We did not have sex as such, but hard sucking on her nipples excited us both so much that we instinctively masturbated each other to orgasm.

I was obviously taking far more milk from her than her baby had ever done, because to compensate she began to produce more and more and her breasts became even

254

rounder and fuller, while her nipples gradually became elongated. It was a happy situation for both of us: she needed to be sucked longer and longer, and I had more and more delicious, sweet mother's milk to drink straight from the breast. The only problem was that, as I work on the buses, my job involved shifts and there were times when it became impossible for me to see her twice a day — and yet I couldn't leave her with breasts so full of milk that it became painful for her. So, with her permission, I brought in a good looking young work mate of mine, Dave, who is equally hooked on women's milk.

With no hint of jealousy or possessiveness we each milked her dry once a day. On occasions, when our days off coincided, we milked her together. Her pleasure was visibly doubled at the sight of a mouth round each of her nipples, and two hands rather than one bringing her to orgasm. My pleasure was certainly doubled, as I saw Dave sucking away with drops of Ann's fresh milk oozing from between his lips.

We even spent our holidays away together in order to keep up the rhythm so that she should continue producing milk that she was glad to give and we were more than glad to receive. This idyllic situation lasted for a little over eighteen months, during which her breasts got steadily bigger and her nipples steadily longer. One day she suddenly cried halt, explaining that she was suffering from physical exhaustion, and that she was beginning to be ashamed of her nipples, that Dave and I had transformed into 'a pair of young boys' penises.'

Although she got married six months later, we are still good — but uninvolved — friends.

I am still unmarried, but as I am only twenty-seven, I hope to get married in the future. I shall, however, make sure that my wife is fond of her nipples and will want them taking care of long after she has weaned our first child.

Pete, Bolton

In Praise Of Lust

I first met my wife, Carol, when she was an 18-year-old virgin and I was a 23-year-old medical student with a special interest in female anatomy. I just couldn't wait to get my cock inside her cunt.

At first it seemed as if she was determined to remain a virgin forever, and I remember that she even slapped my face the first time I put my hand on her breasts!

Then one day, when we had been fooling around, I ended up tanning her backside. She became extremely excited and started to French kiss me. I had a powerful erection by that time and actually shot off in my underpants when she started to fondle my cock and balls through my trousers.

Full of lust I pulled her panties down and began to suck and lick her cunt to orgasm. She writhed and moaned beneath me and I soon had another erection. On seeing this she begged me to fuck her and informed me that her brother had some Durex in his bedroom drawer.

Once I had the sheath on my cock I proceeded to try and get it up her cunt. Fortunately I am blessed with a 9″ cock, which at first I had difficulty getting up her hole. But with one final thrust the whole length slipped into her cunt, my balls resting near her buttocks.

I started to move in and out and almost immediately she had her first orgasm . . . followed by another and another. I lost count after three, but she seemed to go on and on. It was unbelievable.

Even after I'd shot my load several times during the night, she still wanted more. I had to give it to her orally between erection and it was hours before she had had enough. I swear she could take a dozen men and still want more.

You can guess it wasn't long before she got pregnant and we had to get married — though of course I would have married her anyway. Even after three years of marriage we still make love almost every day and I have often woken up to find her mouthing my cock or trying to suck me off.

Dave, Liverpool

More Military Cuts!

I've always been interested in the historical side of sex, and read avidly the readers' letters stating that men sometimes removed the cocks of their enemies to limit their sex lives to cunnilingus. Some of the points raised, however, seemed based on vivid imagination rather than historical fact.

The letter in the Christmas issue, after connecting cock chopping and cunnilingus, stated that there is a reference to it in the 'Perfumed Garden.' The passage actually refers to the execution of a man whose severed penis was stuffed into his mouth before he was hanged for a sex crime. There is no connection with cunnilingus.

Pricks were indeed cut off for the purpose referred to by your readers, but the origin of the practice concerned the economics of warfare and did not even involve live victims. Warriors were often paid a bounty depending on the number of enemy each man had slain in battle. Before payment, proof of the kill was required, usually part of the body. Fingers, ears, clothing, etc., were unacceptable as they would enable several men to claim the same victory. Because of this, and to prevent women being harmed, the male penis became the naturally accepted trophy.

Several penises were skewered into long, curved spikes, which warriors jealously guarded by wearing them at their belts until redeemed for payment. To prevent men removing cocks from their own fallen comrades, it became necessary to make them different from the enemy's, and this is believed to be one of the origins of circumcision.

The difficulty in removing a penis in the heat of battle, must have been instrumental in this particular bounty system's demise.

As giggling sixth-form girls know, castration by cutting off the testicles became the communal punishment for the losing side of a war. It was as a variation of this that penile removal later returned, as your readers correctly assume, to cause frustration and humiliation.

The social impacts would have been extremely varied.

As the victims were still able bodied, the effects on agriculture and commerce would have been insignificant compared with what they would have been if every man had been put to death. The impacts on women must have been very complex indeed. Mixed with obvious compassion for the men, women must have experienced a feeling of independence, possibly superiority, in the knowledge that they alone were still sexually intact and able to enjoy orgasm.

The effects on males must have been devastating. Apart from the pain risk and the ridiculous appearance of balls without a cock, there were great psychological impacts. Until recently, cunnilingus was taboo — an unthinkable act. A man compelled to relinquish his penis was humiliated by the fact that everyone knew he would eventually have to kneel in front of a woman with his head between her thighs. As for frustration, a minute fraction of this can be experienced by any man by sucking off a lady for as long as possible before mounting her. Few men can manage more than a few minutes before lust compels them to substitute prick for tongue.

As frustration results from the continued function of the balls, one can wonder if the Chinese were perhaps less cruel by removing the lot — cock, balls and scrotum. It must have simplified the sex lives of those concerned.

One Red Indian tribe went further in their treatment of any white man foolish enough to be captured. They too cut off the lot, but, instead of chucking the bits away they fed them to him!

Turning to cunnilingus, there must be numerous readers who have not yet enjoyed this beautiful, erotic act. If a woman appears reluctant, the man should be understanding and patient. Most ladies like to 'freshen up' for their lovers and a girl who knows in advance that she may be sucked feels more at ease if she has made preparations.

When dealing with inhibitions, the male should passionately kiss the lady, exploring every corner of her mouth with his tongue, while doing the same to her cunt with his finger. He should then apply wet, tonguing kisses to the inside of her thighs above the stocking tops. If this is done correctly, she will thrust her cunt towards his face while pulling his head towards it.

Cunt sucking is an art. The tongue and lips (but NEVER the teeth) should be used on every part of the cunt, not just the clitoris, and there should be deep thrusts of the tongue into the fuck-hole. The feminine juice is excellent if swallowed.

Hygiene is important. A mouth contains more germs than a cunt and the man should use a mouthwash, which he should then thoroughly rinse out with clean water before commencing. A woman can wash, if she wishes, but she should not use a vaginal deodorant as this can mask her feminine scents which are an aphrodisiac. Under no circumstances should a woman allow a man with cold sores, mouth infections, or spots near the nose and lips to suck her.

Sucks can be carried out on a bed, but the best position is with the lady in an easy chair with her legs wide apart, and the male kneeling with an arm around each leg. If she wears stockings and suspenders, and/or frilly, open-crotch knickers, the feeling of eroticism is enhanced.

If performed correctly, cunnilingus will give the male a pounding heart, heavy breathing, an aching erection and mind-blowing LUST. He will feel as if he is worshipping the lady, who in turn should feel like a Greek goddess.

Ralph, Loughborough

Let no one say this magazine is uninformative — Ed.

Hands That Do Dishes
I would like to share with other readers the expertise of my luscious wife, but only in print! She has a beautiful body, small pert breasts, petite waistline and a lovely arse that makes her just heaven to screw from behind — but when she dresses in black bra, open-crotch briefs,

suspender belt, stockings and black skin-tight thigh boots it's absolutely devastating.

My reason for writing is to tell of my 'wet dream' of a few weeks ago. I went to bed early while my wife watched a film on TV and I fell asleep within minutes. The next thing, in my unconscious state, it felt as though wonderful things were being done to my naughty bits: it was like a dream of heaven which I can't explain, but my balls were aching and my penis felt like it would explode at any minute. On and on it went until a beautiful warm feeling swept through me, then I shuddered and sat up with a start.

My wife was sitting between my legs, a wicked grim spread across her face and those bright red lips teased my manhood with their beckoning. Her breasts stood erect in the dim light of the dressing table, and those legs were encased in tight black leather.

She smiled wickedly at me and said, 'It's OK lovely, you relax and enjoy this one'. I shuddered with pure animal pleasure, and then my eyes nearly popped out as I looked down and saw my penis being slowly wanked to distraction by her bright red rubber-gloved hands which were thick with vaseline. I tried to protest, feeling almost embarrassed, but it was divine and she said, 'There's many out there who'd love it if they got this treatment from me'. I could only agree.

As she put more vaseline on those lovely bright red gloves and pumped away, I tried to hang on, but I couldn't and soon my sperm shot away above my head before subsiding to a normal flow. But still she kept pumping away and greasing my balls: she was in command, and she knew it. Soon I was a quivering mass, lying knackered on the bed — but what a way to go!

It's a religion with her now, but I'm more than willing to go along with it. As soon as I see those gloves going on, I know I'm in for a going over. The only problem is, I can never look at her the same when she's washing up!

After reading the article in July's Fiesta about rubber,

leather etc., she wants me to buy her a skin-tight red latex mini dress, and open-crotch knickers to go with her boots. I dream of walking along the banks of our local river late one summer's evening with her dressed like that, though I'm sure I wouldn't be the only one in the queue, and then taking her from behind in the moonlight. At present that's only a dream but I think you'll agree I have a lady in a million. And I aim to keep her.

E.C., Kent

Tongue Tied

I was disappointed with the article in Vol. 17 No. 1 concerning cunnilingus. Your writer seems unable to convey adequately the unspeakable delights which a man may experience in this most intimate of sex acts, which in my view is wholesome and beautiful. I believe that it belongs to the total and permanent man-woman relationship where a man truly worships his partner — ideally marriage.

From the moment when my wife allows my hand to rest on the springy mat of her pubic hair and my fingers begin to explore the moist cleft, all my cares are behind me. The magic of making contact with her clitoris never fades. It thrills me more and more — and I've been married for thirty years or so.

The lovely resilient morsel is teased by my fingers, but my lips and tongue are jealous of my fingers, for I want to smell and taste my dear wife no less than I want to touch her — but she will not yield to that delight for a while.

I fondle her breasts with the other hand, finding all the old thrills that I knew when she first allowed me to touch them many years ago. The nipples rise and press into my open palms. I roll them gently between finger and thumb until my wife draws my head close to her so that I can suck.

Once, many years ago, I tasted her milk. What a

blessed moment that was. No sooner have my lips drawn her nipples to their full glory than she draws me towards her parted thighs so that I can bury my lips in the fragrant flesh — so like a flower, and my tongue like that of a honey bee.

The scent of a woman's vaginal area is perhaps the most delectable, passion-arousing thing on this earth. It is for me. My penis is sustained to a glorious erection by the delight of the scent, taste and intimate tongue contact with my wife's genitals, so that when she begs me to penetrate her, my passion is wild and abandoned. Cunnilingus? I don't think your article did it justice.

Blissful Reader, London

In The Deep End

I have heard of several couples experimenting with deep-throat techniques and giving up in despair because the girl gagged and became scared of choking. My experience fairly recently has now overcome this problem, and may be of interest to all those who have attempted this wonderful experience and failed to achieve their goal.

First of all I should explain that my husband had not been successful in persuading me to put my lips over his penis, because I have never considered an uncircumcised prick attractive to suck. Before I would allow him to put his penis in my mouth I insisted that he would have to be circumcised. He took some time to agree to my wishes, but with the promise of being sucked off, he finally parted with his foreskin at the age of 26. At first he hated the result but has now come to prefer it.

Within a month of his operation I had started to kiss and suck his penis . . . I had tasted his sperm before he was circumcised by sucking my fingers after wanking him, so the flavour was not new to me. Now that the rolls of sticky red foreskin were gone, I found I was hooked on sucking him at every opportunity. His naked tip seems irresistible to my lips.

Taking fellatio a stage further was only a natural desire. I tried the suggested method of trying to breathe with one or more of my fingers down my throat, but it made me feel sick. I started using a banana, which I found softer and more suitable for the practice. When I could insert the banana gently and remove it without gagging, I then tried a 7″ by 1½″ vibrator, using only the tip. I never tried it with the thing switched on!

Slowly at first, I allowed Robin's knob to touch my throat and push very gently. It is best if the man lies on his back, and the girl keeps hold of his prick while she lowers her mouth over his knob. If he tries to push, a sharp jerk back on his prick will keep matters under control.

It becomes easier as you progress, although in our case Robin's knob has increased in size considerably since losing the constriction of his foreskin. If you try this system, you will find it a really incredible experience once you have perfected the technique.

Joanna, Somerset

STAR BOOKS BESTSELLERS

GOR SERIES

TARNSMAN OF GOR	John Norman	£1.80*
OUTLAW OF GOR	John Norman	£1.80*
PRIEST-KINGS OF GOR	John Norman	£2.25*
NOMADS OF GOR	John Norman	£2.25*
ASSASSINS OF GOR	John Norman	£2.50*
RAIDERS OF GOR	John Norman	£2.25*
CAPTIVE OF GOR	John Norman	£2.35*
HUNTERS OF GOR	John Norman	£2.25*
MARAUDERS OF GOR	John Norman	£2.50*
TRIBESMEN OF GOR	John Norman	£2.35*
SLAVE GIRL OF GOR	John Norman	£2.50*
BEASTS OF GOR	John Norman	£2.60*
EXPLORERS OF GOR	John Norman	£2.50*
FIGHTING SLAVE OF GOR	John Norman	£2.50*
ROGUE OF GOR	John Norman	£2.25*
GUARDSMAN OF GOR	John Norman	£2.50*
SAVAGES OF GOR	John Norman	£2.25*
BLOOD BROTHERS OF GOR	John Norman	£2.50*
KAJIRA OF GOR	John Norman	£2.50*
PLAYERS OF GOR	John Norman	£2.50*
MERCENARIES OF GOR	John Norman	£2.50*

STAR Books are obtainable from many booksellers and newsagents. If you have any difficulty tick the titles you want and fill in the form below.

Name _____

Address _____

_____

Send to: Star Books Cash Sales, P.O. Box 11, Falmouth, Cornwall, TR10 9EN.

Please send a cheque or postal order to the value of the cover price plus: UK: 55p for the first book, 22p for the second book and 14p for each additional book ordered to the maximum charge of £1.75.

BFPO and EIRE: 55p for the first book, 22p for the second book, 14p per copy for the next 7 books, thereafter 8p per book.

OVERSEAS: £1.00 for the first book and 25p per copy for each additional book.

While every effort is made to keep prices low, it is sometimes necessary to increase prices at short notice. Star Books reserve the right to show new retail prices on covers which may differ from those advertised in the text or elsewhere.

*NOT FOR SALE IN CANADA

STAR BOOKS ADULT READS

FICTION

BEATRICE	Anonymous	£2.25*
EVELINE	Anonymous	£2.25*
MORE EVELINE	Anonymous	£2.25*
FRANK & I	Anonymous	£2.25*
A MAN WITH A MAID	Anonymous	£2.25*
A MAN WITH A MAID 2	Anonymous	£2.25*
A MAN WITH A MAID 3	Anonymous	£2.25*
OH WICKED COUNTRY	Anonymous	£2.25*
ROMANCE OF LUST VOL 1	Anonymous	£2.25*
ROMANCE OF LUST VOL 2	Anonymous	£2.25*
SURBURBAN SOULS VOL 1	Anonymous	£2.25*
SURBURBAN SOULS VOL 2	Anonymous	£2.25*
DELTA OF VENUS	Anais Nin	£1.60*
LITTLE BIRDS	Anais Nin	£1.60*
PLAISIR D'AMOUR	A.M.Villefranche	£2.25
JOIE D'AMOUR	A.M.Villefranche	£2.25